First Hundred Years
of Engineering Education
in the United States (1807-1907)

By

JAMES GREGORY McGIVERN, *Sc. D., Ed. D.*
Dean of the School of Engineering
Gonzaga University

GONZAGA UNIVERSITY PRESS
SPOKANE, WASHINGTON

TO
FRANCES

bound by
ARTS & CRAFTS BOOK MFG CO.

ACKNOWLEDGMENTS

The writer wishes to take this opportunity to express his appreciation to the many people who have so kindly assisted him in this work.

For giving original direction to the undertaking he is indebted to Dr. William Crawford, Dr. Raymond Muse, Dean John P. Spielman and Dr. Albert Waterman of Washington State University. For assistance in editing and proofreading he is grateful to Dean Donaldson, the Reverend Charles Keenan, S.J., and Dr. John Sisk of Gonzaga University.

Much of the research material was obtained through Inter-Library Loan Service. The many articles and texts used were arranged for by Mrs. Ruth Seelhammer of the Crosby Memorial Library at Gonzaga University. For the final form of the text and printing arrangements, acknowledgment is due to Leo Aspenleiter, Manager of the Gonzaga University Press.

Final thanks are accorded to the Very Reverend John P. Leary, S.J., President of Gonzaga University, who has sponsored the printing of this book as one of a group to be published by the University as a part of its 75th Anniversary activities.

TABLE OF CONTENTS

LIST OF TABLES

chapter 1

Introduction

General Statement of Problem:—As a peculiar product of the American culture, engineering education has assumed an important place in the American higher educational system. This status is the result of 150 years of an evolutionary growth as a part of private colleges and universities, private technological institutes and state colleges and universities. Many facets of this development have been studied periodically, as evidenced by the Mann report of 1918, the Society for the Promotion of Engineering Education Investigation of 1923 and the more recent "Grinter Report" of 1954. These studies have been concerned with specific aspects of engineering education without providing a strong historical setting of the complete problem. Since no complete study of the subject has been undertaken, it is proposed to give the historical setting and development of engineering education up to the year 1907. By 1907 the character and type of the present day institutions had been established.

Specific Statement of the Problem.—The study is concerned with a chronological development of engineering education in the United States as a result of cultural, industrial, educational, political and professional pressures up to the year 1907. Considered under these topics are technical educational philosophies, contributions of leaders, community and national needs, professional societies, and institutions and educational methodology such as curricula and degree requirements. Viewed differently this study may be thought of as a search for answers to such specific questions as:

1. What are the origins of the American engineering school?
2. What was the effect of the traditional classical college on the development and final status of American engineering schools?
3. How were the establishment and existence of American engineering schools dependent upon initial leadership and local support?
4. How did the growth of the engineering school relate to the industrial needs of the society?
5. How many different types of engineering schools developed?

1

6. How did the establishment and control of engineering education differ from that of the professions of Law and Medicine?
7. What was the evolution of the engineering curriculum up to 1907?
8. How have the professional societies paralleled the growth of the engineering schools?
9. What effect did the "Morrill Act" have on the growth of the engineering education?
10. What relation existed between the growth of American public education and American engineering education?

Material for the Study.—The material presented was obtained from a survey and correlation of existing literature pertaining both directly and indirectly to engineering education. In addition to the direct material many other classifications of literature were examined. These include biographies, college histories, college catalogues, economic studies, and texts and articles on other segments of the American education system.

Method of Presentation.—The study is divided into six stages or time periods. The first or "Pre-1800 Stage" sets the European and American background for the beginning of engineering education in the United States. The second stage (1800-1835) considers the early proposals that were not realized, the development of West Point Military Academy, the history of two short-lived schools, and the founding of Rensselaer Polytechnic Institute. In order to understand the type of people who anticipated America's needs at such an early period, the strong part played by outstanding individuals of the period is described.

The third or "Definition Stage (1835-1864)" describes in some detail the founding of a small number of engineering schools. Here the emphasis is placed on the method of establishment and on the type of institutional structure developed by the institutions. The term, Definition Stage, is adopted as descriptive because in this period the basic types of present day institutional forms were developed. The fourth or the "Rapid Growth Stage (1864-1876)" considers the increase in the number of engineering schools from approximately 8 to 75 in number. Emphasized is the "Morrill Act" and the part it played in providing a means for supporting an educational service demonstrated as needed by the American people.

The fifth division is termed "Continued Growth and Refinement Stage (1876-1892)" and spans the years between the Philadelphia Exposition and the World's Fair at Chicago. This was a period of curricula development for Mining, Mechanical, and Electrical engineering that supplemented the Civil engineering courses offered in the earlier periods. The rise of professional consciousness in the form of many technical societies is of further interest. The concluding or "Evaluation Stage (1892-1907)" marks the beginning of a serious analysis of engineering education in a framework that was already established. The year 1907 was selected as terminal because in that year co-operative education was inaugurated. This innovation marked the end of any major changes in engineering education for a period of approximately twenty years.

It is hoped that this history of the first century of American engineering education will provide a basis to re-orient the thinking of present trends in terms of basic historic patterns and to provide norms for anticipating certain reactions to contemplated changes in the present system.

chapter **2**

Science and Engineering Schools
Prior to 1800

Chapter Introduction

Although entitled "Science and Engineering Schools Prior to 1800," this chapter does not contain a detailed account of the many engineering accomplishments up to this time. This does not deny the importance of early irrigation and surveying practices; the structures, monuments and hydraulic works of the Egyptians and Babylonians; the architecture of the Greeks; nor the roads, buildings and aqueducts of the Romans. What is assumed is that a detailed knowledge of these contributions is not necessary to understand the many influences that affected the structure and practices of the early American engineering schools.

All that is included are the European and American backgrounds necessary to evaluate the origin and purposes of the variety of types of American engineering schools founded in the early nineteenth century. This category considers the modern engineer, the Medieval Universities, the early scientific societies, and the early apprentice system and technical schools. When possible, some of the more important political, social, economic and cultural elements of the various societies which affect the problem will be mentioned. It is this last concept that makes it possible to explain why England, with practically no technical institutions, transformed her economic life through industrialization, while France, with her well developed technical schools, was backward in developing manufacturing and internal improvements.

In America, too, it is necessary to view the development of engineering education in the framework of the political-economic structure and the rewards offered to stimulate local manufacturing and internal improvements. In addition, a sketch of the early American educational system and the social, agricultural, and industrial environment are presented, to give as wide a base as possible to evaluate the origins and justifications of our early American engineering schools.

4

Engineering Prior to Middle Ages

Vitruvius the Roman Engineer.—Marvis defines the architecture of Vitruvius' times as the common ancestor of today's engineer and architect.[1] In this sense he may be classified as one of the first, if not the first, engineer whose works have been well authenticated. At the time of Augustus he designed basilicas, aqueducts, and powerful war machines capable of hurling rocks weighing three or four hundred pounds.[2] Although a cultured and diligent student of Greek philosophy, his main interests were practical. He used geometry to help plan staircases; a knowledge of tones for discharging catapults; law for establishing boundary lines; and hygiene for assistance in selecting building sites with respect to air, water, and sewage disposal. With all the roads and structures that stand as permanent monuments to his genius, Vitruvius is best remembered for his ten short books on architecture.

In volume one of the above mentioned set, he states how an architect, who resembles our present engineer, should be trained. His statement is, in effect, that engineers

> . . . who without culture aim at manual skill cannot gain prestige corresponding to their labors, while those who trust to theory and literature obviously follow a shadow and not reality. But those who have mastered both, like men equipped in full armour, soon acquire influence and attain their purpose.[3]

To show how completely he applied knowledge to the art of design, an examination of his books shows treatment of such topics as building materials; public buildings; interior decorations; machines, including windmills, windlasses, axles and pulleys; and hydraulic engineering. This material possesses the elements of a sound engineering curriculum for the times.

To illustrate that Roman engineering was almost as distinguished as Roman law, Sedgwick and Tyler quote the following as the writing of the Emperor Constantine of the fourth century:

> We need as many engineers as possible. As there is a lack of them, invite to this study persons of about 18 years, who have already studied the necessary sciences. Relieve the parents of taxes and grant the scholars sufficient means.[4]

With the collapse of the Roman Empire, construction was practically discontinued; and the work of Vitruvius, along with other contributions of

---

[1] F.T. Marvis, "History of Engineering Education," *Journal of Engineering Education* (Dec., 1952) Vol. 23, No. 4, p. 216.

[2] W. Libby, *An Introduction to the History of Science* (Cambridge: Houghton Mifflin Company, 1917) p. 30.

[3] Frank Granger (ed. and trans.) *Vitruvius on Architecture* (Book I, Vol 1; Cambridge: Harvard University Press and William Heineman Ltd., 1947).

[4] W. T. Sedgwick and H.W. Tyler, *A Short History of Science* (New York: Macmillan Co., 1937) p. 158.

early times, was not used or added to for some time. A new era of history was necessary before an actual curriculum and school of engineering was to be established. During the intervening period, considerable basic science was to be developed; and education on a more formal basis was to be inaugurated with the founding of the Universities and Scientific Societies of Europe.

Early Universities and Scientific Societies

Medieval Universities.—During the Medieval and Renaissance periods, technical education as such made no progress. There was, however, an intense interest in classical learning, as attested to by the large numbers attending the universities of the time. The enrollments quoted for these schools vary considerably, depending upon the source and authority used. Some of the highest estimates given for the end of the 13th century are 10,000 to 20,000 at the University of Bologna and 30,000 at the Universities of Paris and Oxford.[5] The lower estimates have reduced these numbers, allowing Paris and Bologna 4,000 to 5,000 and Oxford 2,000 to 3,000 students.[6] These figures are not intended to evaluate the size of the universities, but to show that a number of schools of considerable size were in existence. It is probable that a larger proportion of the population received a university education at the close of the Middle Ages than is now thought to be the case.

These universities were for the most part church-created and made up of faculties of philosophy, theology, law and medicine, although mathematics, taught with particular reference to astronomy, was not uncommon. Thus, we have Roger Bacon (1214-1292) studying at the Universities of Oxford and Paris; Copernicus (1473-1543) at the Universities of Carcow, Bologna, and Padua; Galileo (1564-1642) at the University of Pisa; Tycho Brahe (1546-1630) at the University of Copenhagen; and Johann Kepler (1571-1630) attending the University of Tubingen. Although the universities trained leaders in science, they offered no studies in applied science or engineering. For medieval times the faculties of philosophy, theology, and law (Cannon Law) were understandable. The elevation of the science and the art of medicine to faculty status is not so easily explained as Finch would imply:

> Through a curious combination of circumstances, medical schools were part of the earliest university organizations. Actually, there was little in common between the interests of such schools and the ideals of letters and learning which the university title denotes.[7]

[5] Samuel G. Williams, *The History of Medieval Education* (Syracuse, New York: 1903) p. 121.

[6] J. B. Berry, (Planned by) *The Cambridge Medieval History* (New York: Macmillan, 1936) p. 60.

[7] J. K. Finch, The Engineering Profession in Evolution," *Transactions of the American Society of Civil Engineers*, Volume CT, 1953, p. 120.

The above statement indicates the early origin of the medical and law schools as purely professional units having their own faculties. Had these times accorded the engineer the status the Romans conferred on him seven hundred years earlier, it is entirely possible that engineering education would have been incorporated into the university structure. Had this been true the entire history of engineering education would have been different.

Medieval Scientific Societies.—During the period mentioned above, the number of people concerned with Natural Philosophy was rapidly increasing. This interest was reflected in the establishment of societies or academies providing a local, national and international fellowship for those interested in coordinating, disseminating, and advancing scientific knowledge. The earliest of these societies was founded in Naples (1560) under the name of Academia Secretorum Naturae.[8] The academy to which Galileo belonged existed from 1603 to 1830 in Rome, as Academia die Licei; another, founded in 1656 by the Medici in Florence, was known as the Academia Del Cimento. In England the Royal Society was formally incorporated in 1662, and in France the Academie des Sciences in 1666. In 1700 Leibnitz was instrumental in the establishment of the Prussian Academie der Wissenschaften at Berlin,[9] and the Russian Academy of Sciences was opened at St. Petersburg in 1725.

These universities and scientific societies offered little of direct value toward founding or advancing the art of engineering. They did, however, further mathematics and other basic science concepts that gradually evolved into a body of knowledge to be known as the engineering sciences. Rather than being the product of a university-trained profession, the many engineering structures of antiquity, of the Middle Ages, and of the Medieval periods were the results of three influences. In some cases these influences acted separately and at other times together. These three may be enumerated as: the application of art to construction methods that extravagantly used both materials and labor; the works of men of outstanding ingenuity such as Archimedes, Vitruvius, and Leonardo da Vinci; and thirdly those projects resulting from the fusion of known science with construction methods. An example of this latter method is accredited to Tresaquet in France about 1764.[10] In this scientific approach to road building he developed a method improved upon by Telford in England in 1820 and by Macadam, a Scottish engineer in 1818. These beginnings of our modern development of engineering do not deny a lost art practiced before the recording of history. One such example of this is the traces of a sewer arch at Neppur, India, which was probably constructed about

---

[8] W. C. Dampier, *A History of Science* (London: Cambridge University Press, 1947) p. 149.

[9] Libby, *op. cit.,* p. 132.

[10] A. G. Bruce and J. Clarkeson, *Highway Design and Construction* (3rd ed.; Scranton, Pennsylvania: International Text Book Company, 1950) p. 30.

3750 B.C. Another sewer running under an important street in Tell Asmah near Bagdad, "which connected with bath rooms and toilets by tile pipes,"[11] was probably constructed during the twenty-sixth century B.C.

If engineering was born at the time of the Roman civilization, it may be considered to have had a rebirth in France during the reign of Louis XIV. John Colbert, as Comptroller General of Finance under Louis XIV developed commerce, manufacturing and a system of internal communications by water and by land. The Languedoc Canal, 150 miles long, connecting the Mediterranean Sea and the Atlantic Ocean was completed in 1681 as part of his program.[12]

Under Louis XV (1715-1754) the advancement of internal improvements was continued, and for this work he created a special division of the government. This agency was extended to include a school, with the result that it was in France under a strong national foundation that the first school of engineering was founded. It should be noted that the French school thus established had an entity of its own, with no origins in the Medieval Universities or in the well established scientific societies then in existence. It was founded as an arm of the government to train men to improve the transportation facilities of France. A more detailed discussion of this development follows.

The French Technical Schools

Ecole des Ponts et Chaussees.—In France the Royal Corps des Ponts et Chaussees as a division of the government dates back to the thirteenth century. This organization came into prominence in 1747 when Louis XV (1715-1754) made Perronnet chief engineer of bridges and highways. He was appointed to assist in repairing the economic system of France through the construction of a vast network of national highways. In assuming this position he was especially charged:

> With the direction and supervision of surveyors and designers of plans and maps of the roads and highways of the realm and of all those who are appointed and nominated to said work; and to instruct the said designers in the sciences and practices needful to fulfilling with competency the different occupations relating to the said bridges and highways.[13]

The above directive gave Perronnet the authority to establish within his organization and as an appendage of the Corps des Ponts et Chaussees a

---

[11] Anon, "Sewers Forty-Five Hundred Years Ago," *Public Works* (Feb., 1944) p. 35.
[12] J. E. Walkins, "The Beginning of Engineering," *Transactions of the American Society of Civil Engineers* (Vol. 24, 1891) p. 329.
[13] W. E. Wickenden, "A Comparative Study of Engineering Education in the United States and in Europe, Report of the Investigation of Engineering Education 1923-1929," *Society for the Promotion of Engineering Education*, (Vol. 1) p. 758.

school of engineering. This he did in an ingenious manner, as indicated by the following orders issued by him on December 11, 1747:

> That these employees shall be divided into three classes; the first composed of under-instructors or under-engineers; the second of employees called *eleves;* and the third of young men of less education who are admitted to work in the office as auxiliaries.
>
> That the employees of these three classes not otherwise employed will report to the office of Perronnet daily, Sundays and holidays excepted, from eight to noon and from two to eight.
>
> That exceptional rewards will be given to the three most proficient employees of each class, who are to follow the courses of professors of mathematics and architecture indicated by Perronnet.
>
> That during the summer, the employees are to be distributed among the principal works in progress, to execute maps and plans.[14]

The regular students were employees of the state, and the instruction was accomplished by outside professors, by leading engineers of the Corps, and by students of the highest class instructing their juniors. The program of study was three years in length; and the school, maintaining its original program, was legally regularized in 1775 under the name Ecole des Ponts et Chaussees. In 1798 the name was changed to Ecole Nationale des Ponts et Chaussees and it became one of the schools of instruction attached to the Ecole Polytechnique.[15]

This French example of creating a higher technical school distinct from the universities was followed by other European countries and by our early American engineering schools. In addition to this contribution, France was also remarkable in the variety of prototypes of scientific education produced. These other institutions were the Ecole de Mines, Ecole d'Arts et Metiers, Conservatoire des Arts et Metiers, Ecole des Travaux Publics, Ecole Centrale, and the Ecole Polytechnique.

Ecole des Mines.—In 1778 the creation at the Paris mint of a free public school of mineralogy, assaying and metallurgy was authorized. When in 1783 an official Corps des Ingenieurs des Mines was created to promote and regulate the mineral industries of France, the school at the mint became the Ecole des Mines. This development was similar to that of the Ecole des Ponts et Chaussees. This school of mines became one of the models used when Columbia University established its school of mines in the next century. The French school held consistently to scientific discipline and made no effort to reproduce industrial operations in the laboratories. It was maintained that the art must be learned where practiced, and this was provided for by placing the students in the mines during the long vacations.

[14] *Ibid.,* p. 759.
[15] M. M. Chambers (ed.) *Universities of the World Outside U.S.A.* Menasha Wisconsin: George Banta Publishing Company, 1950) p. 365.

Ecole National d'Arts et Metiers.—In 1788 the Duc de Rochefoucauld founded an industrial school for the sons of the non-commissioned officers of his regiment. This became the original mechanic arts type of engineering school that was introduced into this country by Dr. Thompson when he set up the original curriculum of the Worcester Polytechnic Institute.[16] The French school was nationalized in 1799, and in 1803 Napoleon gave it the name Ecole National d'Arts et Metiers, with the purpose of training shop superintendents.

Conservatoire des Arts et Metiers.—An institution incorporating four scientific functions into one was originated by Vaucanson, a master mechanic, and bequeathed to the nation at his death in 1782. It consisted of : (1) a museum of applied science, (2) a public scientific library, (3) a group of free courses in applied science and (4) a group of public laboratories for tests and research. This institution was not actually made a school of technical instruction till 1819, and this aspect of its work has been devoted to training professional engineers and qualified personnel for the higher industrial positions.[17]

The applied science museum continued to expand after the death of its founder, and under the directorship of M. de Vandermounde its collections were increased by five hundred machines between the years 1785 and 1892.[18] This idea of a scientific museum has only lately been introduced into this country, and the use of the facilities of American technical schools for tests and research was not popular until at least one hundred years after the French school initiated the idea.

Ecole Polytechnique.—To compensate for some of the poor training resulting from the disorganization accompanying the French revolution, the Ecole des Travaux Publics was established in 1794 to train engineers for public and private service. This was to be a central school in Paris and was to be supplemented by an Ecole Centrale in each of the provincial capitals. These institutions were discontinued after a year, only to be reborn again in 1829. It was the Ecole Centrale that was to be later used as a norm for reorganization of the curriculum of Rensselaer Polytechnic Institute in 1849.[19]

The single institution replacing the Ecole des Travaux Publics and the Ecole Centrale was the Ecole Polytechnique Institute. This institution soon became the most outstanding scientific school in the world. Entrance was based on severe competitive examinations composed chiefly of mathematics. It had on its staff a brilliant group of creative men. Gaspard Monge, the father of

[16] R. H. Thurston, "Technical Education in the United States," *Transactions of the American Society of Mechanical Engineers,* (Vol. 14, 1893) p. 931.

[17] R. H. Thurston, *Report of New Jersey State Commission* (Trenton; 1878) p. 28.

[18] R. H. Thurston, *op. cit.,* p. 885.

[19] P. C. Ricketts, *History of Rensselaer Polytechnic Institute* (New York: John Wiley and Company, 1934) p. 95.

descriptive geometry, supported the revolution and was the dominating figure in organizing the school. Some of the faculty members well known for their contributions were Lagrange and Laplace in mathematics, Prony in mechanics, Hachette in descriptive geometry, Delorme and Baltard in architecture, and Lourcroy and Berthollet in chemistry.[20] These men and their successors did much to enrich the technical literature that was first used in the French schools. The method of instruction emphasized fundamental science the first two years, with condensed engineering courses in the third year. Later the training in engineering was discontinued and the course became preparatory for entering one of the engineering schools, such as the Ecole des Ponts et Chaussees, which developed curricula that were purely professional in nature.[21]

The German Technical Schools

Bergakademie and the Bauakademie.—In Germany the growth of technical education was very slow and with two exceptions very little was accomplished prior to the nineteenth century. This delay was caused by the lack of organization between the separate states and by the delay caused by attempts to incorporate technical training into the universities under the Latin name "comerage." The first attempt of this nature was in 1773, when applied mathematics was taught at Halle. At about the same time a start in teaching applied science was made at Heidelberg and Gottingen. These efforts were declared foreign to the purposes of the universities, with the result that, as in France, any new institution had to be conceived independently of the existing universities.

Independently of the above attempts, a school of mines known as the Royal Bergakademie was established at Freiberg in the year 1703. This academy was founded for the specific purpose of training mining engineers for work in the Saxon mines. The school was a direct outgrowth of the work of Agricola, who in the sixteenth century helped to establish at Freiberg a central course of mining and metallurgical knowledge.[22]

Agricola is known as the father of metallurgy and published his work, De Re Metallica, in 1556. This work was divided into twelve books and was almost immediately translated from the original Latin into German (1557) and into Italian in 1563. This text served as the basis of the curriculum, but its fame was due to Professor Werner, as Wallbank and Tayler have pointed out:

[20] H. F. Girvin, *A Historical Appraisal of Mechanics* (Scranton, Penn.: International Text Book Company, 1948) p. 227.
[21] S.P. Timoshenko, *History of the Strength of Materials* (New York: McGraw-Hill Company, 1953) p. 58.
[22] Bern Dibner, *Agricola on Metals* (Norwalk, Conn.: Burndy Library, 1958) p. 126.

In 1765 the first mining school in Europe was established in Germany. Nine years later there came to the new institution a professor named Abraham Werner, whose great learning and efficient teaching methods made this school the world center of mineralogy studies.[23] It was this school and the Ecole des Mines of France that were used as models when Columbia University established its school of mines in 1862. The only other school formed in the eighteenth century was the Royal Bergakademie at Berlin in 1799. Both these institutions were government operated, and students were admitted at the age of fourteen with only a common-school education. The course for surveyors was three semesters in length and the one for construction was five. It was not until the next century that Germany developed a distinctly national type of polytechnic school. The first of these new schools was Karlsruhe, which in 1833 was reorganized into a professional school with courses in architecture, civil engineering, and forestry.[24]

Russian Technical Education

Russia was early in the field of technical education under the successive leadership of Peter the Great, his widow Catherine I, his daughter Elizabeth, Catherine the Great and Alexander I. These rulers not only founded schools similar to those in Europe but invited outstanding scientists and teachers from outside Russia to staff them.

In 1707 Peter the Great founded the "School of Navigation and Mathematics," which for a long time served as the center of higher technical education.[25] It was located in Moscow and directed by a Scotchman, Henry Tagwarson, invited to Russia for that purpose.[26] In 1715 the school was moved to St. Petersburg and named the Naval Academy. In addition to the Naval Academy, Peter created engineering and artillery schools, which were staffed with teachers from Great Britain.[27] In 1709 a school in connection with the iron works at Nevia was founded.[28] Prior to his death Peter followed the example of France and Germany and, with the advice of the German scientists Wolff and Leibnitz, made plans for an academy of science at St. Petersburg. This academy was established by his widow Catherine I in 1726 and was made up of associations of learned men and a teaching gymnasium. To give status to the school of the academy, Nicholas and Daniel Bernouilli

[23] T. W. Wallbank and A. M. Tayler, *Civilization Past and Present,* (Chicago: Scott Foresman Company, 1956) p. 245.

[24] H. F. Girvin, *op. cit.,* p. 227.

[25] "Universities of the World Outside the United States," *American Council on Education,* Washington, D.C., 1950, p. 843.

[26] S. Vernadsky, *A History of Russia* (Philadelphia, Penn.: Blakeston Co., 1929) p. 129.

[27] P. Monroe (ed.), *A Cyclopedia of Education* (New York: The Macmillan Co., 1917) p. 229.

[28] T. T. Read, "The Development of Mineral Industry Education in the United States," *Amrican Institute of Mining and Metallurgical Engineers* (New York; 1941) p. 5.

were appointed professors, to be succeeded by Leonard Euler,[29] also of Swiss origin.

In 1755 the University of Moscow was founded, made up of the faculties of Law, Medicine, and Philosophy. This followed the European tradition of excluding engineering training from the university program. In 1773 a School of Mines was established at St. Petersburg.[30] All these schools created during the eighteenth century were government controlled, but did not constitute organized systems of higher education. Such an organization was initiated during the first quarter of the nineteenth century, when Alexander I established five new universities and six higher technical institutions.[31] One of these technical schools, "The Institute of Engineers of Ways and Communication," was established in 1807 and became famous under the influence of Lame and Clapeyron, the Frenchmen who were invited to join the staff of the institute.[32]

This short discussion may be concluded by showing that the Russian technical schools maintained high standards during the nineteenth century. Church, in rating mining schools of the world in 1871, classed the mining school at St. Petersburg as equal, in some respects superior, to those of Paris, Freiberg, and Berlin.[33]

Technical Training in England

The Indenture System.—Education for the trades or the profession in England from the time of Elizabeth until 1814 was acquired by the indenture system. This method, imposed by law, required an apprenticeship of seven years; this system was later replaced by a system of training by pupilage. Under this later pupilage plan the student began at 17 years of age after a grammar school education. The pupil received no pay for his services and the master received an amount varying from 100 to 500 pounds, depending upon his reputation. This accounts for the fact that few of the early English engineers were university graduates. This period of self-made men included such individuals as Brindley, the millwright and early canal builder; Smeaton, the instrument maker and the first man to be termed civil engineer; Metcalf, the blind road-builder; Newcomen, the blacksmith of steam engine fame; Telford, the stone mason; Watt, the instrument maker; Crompton and Hargreaves, the weavers; and Stephenson, the illiterate fireman who learned to read in an evening school.

British industry was, for the most part, the result of the inventiveness

[29] S. P. Timoshenko, *op. cit.*, p. 28.

[30] T. T. Read, *op. cit.*, p. 5.

[31] "Universities of the World Outside the United States," *op. cit.*, p. 843.

[32] H. M. Westegard, "Advance in Structural Analysis" *Transactions of the American Society of Civil Engineers,* 1930, Vol. 94, p. 228.

[33] J. A. Church, "Mining Schools in the United States," *North American Review,* Vol. 62, pp. 62-81.

and interprise of these practical men whose training under the pupilage system entitled them to the title "civil engineer." Their education did not stop at the end of their so-called pupilage period. The first evidence of an organized effort to supply a continuous program of training and comradeship was the efforts of John Smeaton.[34] In March, 1771 he called together 65 engineers for a meeting at King's Head Tavern, London. In addition to Smeaton, such men as Joseph Whitworth, Joseph Priestley, Mathew Bolton, and James Watt made up the group of 15 of the 65 that had professional engineering status. This group was known as the Smeatonians and disbanded after a year due to Smeaton's leadership being challenged. Twenty-one years later, in April, 1793, a new group was formed under the name of the Society of Civil Engineers. Many of the original Smeatonians belonged to this new organization, which was constitutionally limited to 48 engineering members and 12 honorary members. This society is not to be confused with the Institute of Civil Engineers, which was founded in 1818 and was created specifically as a means of mutual education to supplement the training by pupilage. This is stated in the original by-laws of the Institution which prescribed that a member ". . . shall have been regularly educated as a Civil Engineer, according to the usual routine of pupilage."[35]

Royal Technical Institute.—Two exceptions to the above methods of training are to be found in the British Isles during this period. The first was the founding in 1796 of the first school of applied science in the English-speaking world, under the name of the Royal Technical Institute of Glasgow. The second was the establishment in London in 1800 of the Royal Institution of Great Britain. The Glasgow school was the result of a bequest by a John Anderson, a professor at the University of Glasgow, who had employed James Watt as his instrument maker. The London school was the result of a prospectus issued by Count Rumford in 1799. This prospectus was entitled "Proposals for forming by subscription, in the metropolis of the British Empire, a public institution for diffusing the knowledge and facilitating the general introduction of useful mechanical inventions and improvements, and of teaching, by courses of philosophical lectures and experiments, the applications of science to the common purposes of life."[36] Part of the wording as to the purposes of this institution was utilized later in America by Jesse Buel in his proposed law in New York State and by Van Rensselaer when he described the purpose of the new school he caused to be founded.

England and France Compared.—The contrast between the highly developed engineering schools in France and the apprentice system in England

[34] W. R. Woolrich, "Education for Professional Engineering Responsibility," *Journal of Engineering Education* (Vol. 44, 1953) p. 9.
[35] Transactions of the Institute of Civil Engineers, Introduction (Vol. 1, 1836).
[36] P. C. Ricketts, *op. cit.*, p. 4.

was striking. Equally striking were the many engineering accomplishments of England as contrasted to the few French developments. These differences indicate the strength of the many forces outside of technical training methods that determine technological progress. In this case the answer lay in England's stable government, which catered to the interests of the commercial classes. Its policy of keeping the trade routes open provided foreign markets for the surplus goods created by the new factory system. This in turn created capital to be reinvested in the industries created by the new technology. While this was occurring in England, France was engaged in the revolution and the Napoleonic Wars which absorbed all her interests. This thought was expressed by Shortwell when he said ". . . the wars against Napoleon were not won at Leipzig or Waterloo, but rather in the cotton factories of Manchester and the iron mills of Birmingham."[37]

Scientific Instruction in American Colleges Prior to 1800

Preliminary Considerations.—On the basis of the previous material there is little reason to object to Professor Wolf's conclusion that "the vast majority of the pioneers of modern thought were either entirely detached from the Universities, or were but loosely associated with them."[38] Sir Isaac Newton was more often identified with the Royal Society of London than with Trinity College at Cambridge. The history of the major contributions to science for this period is to be found in the Philosophical Transactions and not in curricula, professorships, or academic foundations. This concept has often been applied to the eighteenth century by the application of the yardstick of our present knowledge. In the foreword of a book by I. B. Cohen, Samuel Morison states that Cohen shows that:

> Harvard and her early rivals were well abreast of the science of their day; and that the scientific attitude of mind was inculcated in their students, who had ample apparatus for experiments; and that some of the professors organized scientific expeditions and made positive contributions to knowledge.[39]

The early American engineering schools arose out of a combination of the needs of the time and the scientific atmosphere created by the then existent colleges. This atmosphere was carried over by such men as Benjamin Hale, an 1818 Bowdoin College graduate,[40] who established the Gardiner Lyceum; and Amos Eaton, a 1799 Williams College graduate, who became

[37] H. E. Barnes, *The History of Western Civilization* (New York: Harcourt Brace and Company, 1936) p. 272.

[38] A. Wolf, *A History of Science, Technology, and Philosophy in the Sixteenth and Seventeenth Centuries,* (London: Allen and Univin, 1935) p. 54.

[39] I. B. Cohen, *Some Early Tools of American Science* (Cambridge: Harvard University Press, 1950) p. 10.

[40] "Benjamin Hale," *Dictionary of American Biography,* Vol. 8 (1936) p. 96.

the senior professor at the Rensselaer School. In addition there were college graduates who became engineers such as Eli Whitney, a 1792 Yale graduate,[41] and Hinton James, the first graduate of the University of North Carolina in 1798.[42] James is of interest because the University of North Carolina was the first state university in America, and because he became assistant to Robert Fulton on navigation work, and superintendent of work for improving the Cape River.[43]

These considerations, coupled to the slow adoption of an engineering curriculum, warrant an investigation of what science was being taught in the American College at the end of the eighteenth and the beginning of the nineteenth century.

Colleges of the Early Nineteenth Century.—Hornberger states that a book published in 1803 by Reverend Samuel Miller contains at its end the nearest thing to a directory of American Colleges for that time.[44] From Hornberger's summary of Miller's data, supplemented by material Hornberger gives, the following information is of interest to this investigation.

There were actually twenty-seven colleges chartered in America by the year 1780. Of this number eleven can be immediately dismissed as having practically no influence on the times. This would be due to their short period of operation, as the date of their first classes seldom corresponded to the date of their legal foundation. Of the sixteen colleges remaining, only eight had existence prior to 1780, and the story of collegiate training prior to 1800 can best be told in terms of these eight. These colleges, in the chronological order of their founding, with their respective enrollments for the year 1800, are: Harvard 200, William and Mary 53, Yale 217, University of Pennsylvania 150, Princeton 150, Columbia 125, Dartmouth 140, and Brown 140. The above list does not include, as it should, Rutgers College, which was founded in 1766 as Queen's College. The writer has been unable to determine the accurate enrollment of Queen's for the year 1800, but would place it at approximately 150 students. Nicholas Romayne, M.D., of New York stated in 1792 that for several years he taught medical science to as many as fifty-six students in a class at Queen's College.[45]

The total of the enrollments of these nine colleges was 1,325 and agrees well with the figures quoted by Cubberly who states:

... of the two dozen colleges that existed in 1800, it is estimated that

[41] J. Mershy and A. Nevin, *The World of Eli Whitney* (New York: Macmillan Company, 1952) p. 42.

[42] "Hinton James," *Dictionary of American Biography,* Vol. 5, (1939) p. 605.

[43] F. T. Marvis, *op. cit.,* p. 218.

[44] T. Hornberger, *Scientific Thought in American Colleges 1638-1800* (Austin, Texas: The University of Texas Press, 1945) p. 5.

[45] W. H. S. Demarest, *A History of Rutgers College 1766-1924* (New Brunswick, New Jersey: Rutgers College Press, 1924) p. 180.

they did not have a total of over one hundred instructors and professors, and not less than one thousand or more than two thousand students.[46] To ascertain specifically the science and mathematics offerings of these institutions, the following description for each school is given.

Harvard College.—As early as 1708 one of the four tutors, Thomas Robie, specialized in science and induced the corporation to acquire so much "philosophical apparatus" that a special chamber was assigned to it. He was voted a bonus of 24 pounds in appreciation of his work; and Leverett, the president, at Robie's resignation recorded, "that Mr. Robie was no small honor to Harvard College."[47] In 1727 Thomas Hollis of England founded the Hollis Professorship of Mathematics and Natural Philosophy, with an endowment of 1,200 pounds and the apparatus to go with it. Isaac Greenwood, a pupil of Robie's, was the first incumbent; and for several years, he was a great stimuli to science in the colonies. Greenwood was separated from his alma mater in 1738 due to excessive drinking. Morison states:

> Under his pupil and successor John Winthrop, Hollis Professor from 1738 to 1779, the chair gathered reputation without reproach.[48]

As a great teacher Winthrop introduced four decades of students to the scientific view. Among his students was Count Rumford, who described Winthrop as "an excellent and happy teacher."[49]

Winthrop may also be credited with stimulating Laommi Baldwin, who accompanied Thompson in his walk from Woburn to Cambridge several times a week to attend the lectures in physics and mathematics. Baldwin became famous as a civil engineer and received an honorary A. M. degree from Harvard in 1785.[50]

One particular act of Samuel Williams, who replaced Winthrop as Hollis Professor, illustrated a spirit of scientific inquiry and cooperation not often credited to the eighteenth century. In 1780, which was one of the darkest years of the revolutionary war, Professor Williams, with Stephen Sewall, Professor of Oriental Languages; James Winthrop, the Librarian; Fortesque Verman (A. B. 1779); and Messrs Akins, Daves, Hall, Dawson, Rensselaer, and King (students at the University) led Harvard's second expedition to observe an eclipse of the sun. The observations were made in British territory, with permission, and the galley used to sail down east was borrowed from the Massachusetts Board of War.[51]

---

[46] E. P. Cubberly, *The History of Education* (Boston: Houghton Mifflin Company, New 1920) p. 104.

[47] Samuel E. Morison, *Three Centuries of Harvard* (Cambridge: Harvard University Press, 1936) p. 58.

[48] *Ibid.,* p. 80.

[49] *Ibid.,* p. 93.

[50] "Laommi Baldwin," *Dictionary of American Biography,* Vol. 5 (1936), p. 539.

[51] I. B. Cohen, *op. cit.,* p. 16.

To further emphasize the favorable attitude toward science, it is noted that:

> The faculty at the end of the eighteenth century consisted of four tutors and six professors, in the fields of divinity, mathematics and natural philosophy, rhetoric and oratory, anatomy and surgery, the theory and practice of physics, chemistry and materia medica.[52]

The professor of mathematics and natural philosophy was Samuel Webber, the author of a widely used two volume text on mathematics. This man was elected president of Harvard in 1805 by a vote of 35 to 14 after Fisher Ames had declined the position on the grounds of his feeble health and his advanced age of forty-seven years.[53]

Hornberger reports a remarkable uniformity of the curriculum at Harvard, Yale, Princeton, Brown, North Carolina, and Dartmouth between 1740 and 1800.[54] To illustrate the material covered by these curricula the following vote on September 27, 1791 of the Harvard Corporation and overseers is of interest:

> To animate the students in the pursuit of literary merit and fame, and to excite in their breasts a noble spirit of emulation, there shall be annually a public examination in the presence of a joint Committee of the Corporation and Overseers and such other gentlemen as may be inclined to attend it. The Juniors and Freshmen shall be examined the day preceding the second Wednesday in April, annually, and the Seniors and Sophomores the second Wednesday in May, by the Several Professors and Tutors in their respective departments, as far as each class shall have advanced the preceding years in the following branches of literature, viz.: in the Latin and Greek Classics, the Elements of English Grammar and Rhetoric, those who study Hebrew in the Rudiments of that Language, and those who do not study Hebrew in the French Language, by the French Instructor; in Arithmetic, Logic, Geography, Mensuration, Algebra, and Modern History, English Composition, Belles Lettres, Universal Grammar, the Sphere, Spherical Geometry and Trigonometry, with their application to Astronomical Problems, Natural Philosophy, Astronomy and Theology. And they shall be called upon to answer such questions as the President or any gentlemen of the Committee may suggest.[55]

It was a curriculum such as the above that trained Loammi Baldwin, the son of the friend of Count Rumford. This man graduated from Harvard College in 1800 and was identified with nearly all the outstanding American engineering works for thirty years. Professor George L. Vose says of Baldwin,

---

[52] Hornberger, *op. cit.*, p. 7.
[53] S. Morison, *op. cit.*, p. 190.
[54] T. Hornberger, *op. cit.*, p. 28.
[55] Louis Franklin Snow, *The College Curriculum in the United States* (New York: Teachers College, Columbia University, 1907) p. 88.

"No man so well deserves the name of Father of Civil Engineering in America."[56]

William and Mary College.—The first philosophical chair established was of natural philosophy and mathematics in 1712.[57] This professorship was first held by Mr. Le Lerre who, although discharged for drunkeness after one year of service, had the distinction of being the first man to hold a chair of science in any American college. Nine men serving from one to twelve years held the position up to the time of the revolution. William Small, who served from 1758 to 1764, was the most outstanding; he introduced the lecture system at William and Mary. Upon resigning he returned to England and became associated with James Watt and Erasmus Darwin.

The importance the school attached to science may be indicated by its awarding to Benjamin Franklin the first honorary degree prior to the revolution. In addition, it elected James Madison president in 1777. Madison had previously been professor of natural philosophy and mathematics, and under his direction the college reacted immediately to the changed condition resulting from the winning of political independence.[58] The need for evaluation of the new demands of civil leadership, and the present inadequacy of a course of study that had been worked out hundreds of years ago, was becoming increasingly apparent. At the suggestion of Thomas Jefferson, then governor of Virginia, and under President Madison, the college modernized its curriculum in 1779 and permitted students to elect certain courses and ignore others.[59] This new organization is best explained in a letter to President Stiles of Yale written by President Madison on Aug. 27, 1780, the important part of which reads as follows:

> The Society at present consists of a President, who is always to be one of the Professors, and is now Prof. of Math. and Nat. Phily., 2 of Law and Police, 3 of Chemistry and Medicine, 4 of Ethics and ye Belles Lettres, 5 of Modern Languages .... The Prof. of Humanity has been abolished, the Professorship of Divinity is also abolished. It was formerly instituted for ye purpose of ye Church of England, wh. was here established, but it is now thought that Establishments in Favr. of any particular Sect are incompatible with ye Freedom of a Republic, and therefore, ye Professorship is entirely dropped ... The Doors of ye University are open to all, nor is even a knowledge of ye ant. Languages a previous Requisite for Entrance. The Students have ye Liberty of diffr. Lectures in a term if they think proper.

[56] G. L. Vose, "Sketch and the Life and Works of Loammi Baldwin," *Civil Engineering* (Vol. 14, 1885).
[57] Galen W. Ewing, "Early Teaching of Science at the College of William and Mary in Virginia," *Journal of Chemical Education* (Vol. 15, 1938) p. 3.
[58] George P. Schmidt, *The Old Time College President* (New York: Columbia University Press, 1930) p. 154.
[59] Lyon G. Tyler, *A Few Facts From the Records of William and Mary College,"* in paper of the American Historical Association (Vol. 4; American Historical Association; Oct. 1890)

attending whom they please, and in what order they please, or all ye
The time of taking Degrees was formerly ye same as in Cambridge,
but now depends upon ye Qualification of ye candidate. He has a certain course pointed out for his first Degree, and also for ye rest. When
Master of Either, ye Degree is conferred.[60]

Although a certain degree of freedom was allowed the students, the requirements for the Bachelor of Arts degree in 1792 were specifically stated
as follows:

The student must be acquainted with the 1st, 6th, 11th, and 12th books
of Euclid, plane trigonometry, surveying, algebra, spherics, conic sections; he must have acquired a knowledge of Natural Philosophy as far
as it related to the general properties of matter, mechanics electricity,
pneumatics, hydrostatics, optics, and the first principles of astronomy;
he must be acquainted with logic, the belles lettres, rhetoric, natural
law, laws of nature, and the general principles of politics; he must also
have a competent knowledge of geography and of ancient and modern
languages.[61]

Yale College.—As early as 1749 Professor Stiles engaged in some electrical experiments on a machine contributed to the college by Benjamin
Franklin.[62] Fluxions (calculus) appeared in 1758, and during twenty-five
years thereafter only a few sets of theses lacked problems on this subject.[63]

In 1795 Timothy Dwight replaced Ezra Stiles as president and shaped
the institution's development for a half century or more. He appointed Jere-
miah Day professor of chemistry in 1802. Day was appointed president in
1817 and served in this position for some twenty years. Silliman remained at
Yale until 1853 and in 1818 established the American Journal of Science.[64]
President Dwight appointed Silliman on the basis of his confidence in him; at
the time Silliman had completed his training in law, and he took special training in Chemistry before assuming his professorship.

Just prior to the above appointments in 1800 the faculty consisted of
the president, three tutors, and professors of mathematics and natural philosophy, divinity, and oriental language.[65]

Columbia College.—Columbia had, by the end of the eighteenth century,
a rather complicated structure. It had professors in four distinct fields, one of
which was mathematics and chemistry. In addition it had a medical school
with a dean and four professors.[66] In a 1794 report by Professor Mitchell,

[60] Louis Franklin Snow, *op. cit.,* p. 74.
[61] Galen W. Ewing, *op. cit.,* p. 8.
[62] "Benjamin Franklin," *Dictionary of American Biography,* Vol. 8 (1936).
[63] L. G. Simmons, *Introduction of Algebra into American Schools in the Eighteenth Century,* Bureau of Education Bulletin (Washington, D.C.: 1914, No. 18) p. 38.
[64] Daniel G. Gilman, *The Relations of Yale to Letters and Science* (New Haven: Yale
University Prss, 1902) p. 67.
[65] J. Hornbrger, *op. cit.,* p. 7.
[66] *Ibid.,* p. 9.

the professor of Natural History, a course given by John Kemp, the Professor of Natural Philosophy, is described as containing Mechanics, Hydrostatics, Hydraulics, Pneumatics, Optics, Electricity, Magnetism, and Astronomy. He further states that there were about 600 experiments associated with various courses.[67] To show how the material was distributed, a breakdown of the curriculum offered in 1789 is presented:

> Freshman Class: Twice a week. Extraction of the roots; algebra as far as cubic equations.
> Sophomore Class: Three times a week. Euclid's elements; plane trigonometry, its application to the mensuration of heights and distance of surfaces and solids; land surveying, navigation.
> Junior Class: Once a day. Conic sections and other curves. Projections of the sphere; spherical trigonometry, its application to astronomy; the higher parts of algebra; the application of algebra to geometry, general principle of fluxions.
> Senior Class: Once a day. General properties of matter; laws of motion; mechanical powers, construction of machines; hydrostatics; hydraulics; pneumatics; optics; astronomy; electricity and magnetism.[68]

The organization of the college was such that any student could attend any or all the mathematics, natural philosophy, or astronomy classes without regularly attending or being subject to the regulations of the college. Even before the complete scientific curriculum of 1789 was offered, Columbia graduated an outstanding engineer. This man, John Stevens of the class of 1768, distinguished himself by building steam boats, railroads, and by initiating the patent law.

Princeton College.—Princeton was not averse to having a man with scientific interests as its president. Ashbel Green, a popular professor of Mathematics and Natural Philosophy, resigned in 1787 to accept a call as ministerter of a large church. Twenty-five years later he was to return to the college as its president.[69]

A student could take science and mathematics as part of his regular curriculum, as Wertenbaker states:

> When a youth entered college he could look forward to an introduction into the mysteries of science in his second year, for Burr and his successors followed in the footsteps of the dissenting academies in shifting the emphasis from the classics, logic and metaphysics to mathematics and natural philosophy. Yet they made the privilege of proceeding to the sciences the reward for an early mastery of Latin and Greek.[70]

[67] *Report published in Commemoration of the 150th Anniversary of the Founding of King's College 1904, A History of Columbia University, 1754-1904* (New York: Columbia University Press, 1904) p. 80.
[68] L. F. Snow, *op. cit.,* p. 96.
[69] T. J. Wertenbaker, *Princeton 1746-1896* (Princeton: Princeton University Press, 1946) p. 70.
[70] *Ibid.,* p. 92.

Wertenbaker also makes mention of the fact that in directing students to the sciences the faculty had no fear that they would undermine religion or weaken their faith in the Bible.

As with the other colleges the strength of the faculty in mathematics and science was strong in proportion to the other disciplines. In 1803, the staff consisted of a president, three tutors, and three professors, one in languages, one in divinity, and one in the field of mathematics, natural philosophy and chemistry.[71]

Dartmouth College.—In contrast to the more liberal approach to the curriculum, Dartmouth may be classified as exhibiting the other extreme.

> Once admitted to the institution the student found the curriculum of the college to be as rigid and inexorable as fate; no course was given which was not prescribed to all. For three years, two thirds of the time was devoted to Latin and Greek. The other third was assigned to arithmetic, English grammar, logic, geography, geometry, trigonometry, algebra, conic section, surveying, mensuration, natural and moral philosophy, and astronomy; a multiplicity of subjects acquaintance with any one of which must have been of the slightest.[72]

With the founding of a medical school in 1798, Richardson reports that fifty percent of the juniors and seniors merely paid an extra fee to attend the lectures on medicine. They had no idea of embracing a medical career, but attended the lectures in chemistry and anatomy in a desire to break away from the rigidity of the traditional curriculum. In 1800 the college had a faculty of six, made up of the president; two tutors; and professors in mathematics and natural philosophy, the Latin and Greek languages, and chemistry and medicine.[73]

Dartmouth College graduated in 1807 one of the most outstanding engineering educators in the person of Sylvanus Thayer. Thayer also graduated from West Point in 1809; and, as a superintendent of West Point from 1817 to 1833, he brought the Military Academy into high repute.[74]

Brown University.—The curriculum for the year 1803 contained arithmetic in the freshman year, and algebra and Euclid in the sophomore year. In the junior year, natural philosophy, chemistry, and trigonometry; surveying and navigation were taught in conjunction with the classical subjects. No mathematics or science is listed for the senior year, with the exception of what might be included in the review of preceding studies.[75] A little later, in 1811, Brown University established a Medical School.

71 T. Hornberger, *op. cit.,* p. 8.
72 L. R. Richardson, *History of Dartmouth College* (Vol. 1; Hanover, New Hampshire: Darthmouth College Publication) p. 248.
73 T. Hornberger, *op. cit.,* p. 11.
74 L. R. Richardson, *op. cit.,* p. 541.
75 W. C. Bronson, *The History of Brown University* (Providence Rhode Island: Brown University Press, 1914) p. 167.

In 1800 the faculty consisted of five members including the president; there were three tutors, a professor of law and a professor of mathematics and natural philosophy.[76]

Professional Education in 1800

Colleges Not Hostile to Change.—Although of English origin, the colonial college curricula had, by 1800, developed a pattern that was distinctly American in character. This was exemplified by the surveying and navigation courses commonly taught and referred to previously. These courses of utilitarian value, and the relatively strong emphasis given to mathematics and natural philosophy, indicate that the colleges were not hostile to change. The willingness of these schools to adapt their programs to current needs is further evidenced by the establishment of medical faculties at Harvard in 1789, at the University of Pennsylvania in 1766, and at Columbia in 1807.[77] At the College of William and Mary the first chair of law was founded in 1779. The first appointment to this chair was George Wythe, who had Thomas Jefferson and John Marshall as students.[78] Recognition of the ministry, medicine, and law as warranting special programs is believed to have been based upon their status as professions. It should not be implied that these few schools supplied the total number of members needed for the professions at the time. They did not replace the system of individual apprenticeship under experienced practioners that was inherited from England.

Judge Reeves Law School.—To illustrate professional education outside of the framework of the college, a proprietary law school founded by Judge Reeves at Litchfield is a good example. This school was founded in 1784 and continued approximately fifty years until 1833. Dean Roscoe Pound states that:

> The teachers were practicing lawyers; but they organized the teaching part of their work, laid out a regular course divided into topics, and dictated lectures on each topic, so that in the days of few libraries and almost no law text books, each student could carry away a series of lectures on the main heads of the law, amounting to a set of texts. This was the beginning of one side of all legal education.[79]

Of the 1,023 graduates of this school: 101 became members of congress, 21 U. S. Senators, 34 judges of the higher state court, 10 governors of states, 6 cabinet officers, 3 justices of the federal supreme court, and 2 Vice-President of the United States. As a proprietary school Judge Reeves' school

76 T. Hornberger, *op. cit.,* p. 10.
77 A. Flexner, "Medical Education in the United States and Canada," *Bulletin No. 4 of the Carnegie Foundation for the Advancement of Teaching,* New York, 1910, p. 5.
78 Julius Goebel (ed) *A History of the School of Law Columbia University* (New York: Columbia University Press, 1955) p. 10.
79 Raymond A. Kent (ed) *Higher Education in America* (Boston, Mass.: Ginn and Company, 1930) p. 262.

set an example that a segment of both medical and legal institutions followed for many years. That profit making was the main reason for their existence is mentioned by Goebel: "Some of the American lawyers found the instruction of apprentices more rewarding than practice and took in enough of them to form regular law schools."[80] This practice did not occur in American engineering education, as there is no record of any school growing out of an enlarged pupilage program, as occurred in France when the Ecole des Ponts de Chaussees was established. It should be pointed out that the professional medical and law schools were organized and staffed by members of the respective professions. In this respect they became more or less independent of the curricula of the colleges to which they were attached.

Factors Against Curriculum Changes.—In 1800 the engineering profession in America was not considered one that needed a prescribed curriculum for its preparation. This attitude followed from the English system of pupilage adopted in this country. It could be justified at the time on the basis of the successful economy England developed with the aid of her engineers during the industrial revolution. On the other hand the American engineering profession disregarded the engineering schools successfully operating in France at the beginning of the nineteenth century. In addition to not copying the French type of institution, the American college ignored the developments in pure and applied science subjects commonly taught in France. The science or natural philosophy taught in the American College at the beginning of the 19th century reduced to elementary courses in physics, astronomy, chemistry, and mathematics, which, for the more progressive schools, included calculus. Some of this cultural lag between what was known and what was taught may have been due to the great changes in the philosophy of science at the beginning of the nineteenth century. In chemistry Leicester has the following to say:

> In the latter half of the eighteenth century confusion in chemical thought was at its height. The number of known chemical facts had increased enormously, but the phlogiston theory had failed to keep pace with them. It was the work of Lavoisier that resolved this confusion and placed chemistry on an essentially modern basis.[81]

The reason that the new approach was not taught from a text on elementary chemistry published by Lavoisier in 1789 under the title "La Traite Elementaire de la Chemia"[82] may be traced back to the English example followed by American Colleges. Meyers, speaking of the achievements of Lavoisier in doing away with the old prejudices, states:

The most distinguished chemists in England and Sweden at the time of

[80] Julius Goebel (ed) *op. cit.,* p. 6.
[81] Henry Leicester, *The Historical Background of Chemistry* (New York: John Wiley and Sons, 1956) p. 127.
[82] F. J. Moore, *A History of Chemistry,* (New York: McGraw-Hill Company, 1931) p.56.

Lavoisier's attack upon the phlogiston theory, viz., Black, Cavendish, Priestly, Scheele, and Bergman, were avowed opponents of the new doctrine.[83]

The Royal Institution previously founded by Count Rumford was one school that taught the new scientific theories. This school in the year 1802 had on its staff Humphry Davy, and Thomas Young, and later was to have Michael Faraday as Davy's assistant. Those men were original investigators and were not opposed to change.

In the field of electricity real changes would hardly be expected in the curriculum. It will be remembered that practically all work in electricity up to about 1790 was confined to electrostatics. It was a time for great change which would be reflected in a curriculum of a later date. The beginning was made then:

> Volta continued and extended Galvani's frog experiments and proved the phenomena was due to electricity generated by contact of dissimilar metals and in 1800 gave a description of the first battery for producing an electric current.[84]

From the comments on chemistry and electricity it is understandable that these subjects were not given a larger place in the college curriculum. This reasoning does not explain why European developments in the field of applied mechanics were not adopted by the American colleges. The hydrodynamics of D'Alembert and Bernoulli, the mechanics of Lagrange, the hydraulics of Venturi and Woltman[85] and the elasticity of Coulomb, Young and Euler[86] were not recognized, despite the fact that the material, for the most part, was contained in texts used in the French schools. The reason for the lack of adoption was due in part to lack of confidence in the French engineers, who led in theory but not in any of the new practical developments. This is well stated by a quotation that Finch repeats, "They are highly competent in advanced mathematics and science but haven't a practical hair in their heads."[87] This fact that the basic engineering sciences were not being taught in the colleges or that separate technical schools had not been founded did not mean that Americans were not practicing or contributing to the profession of engineering at the beginning the nineteenth century.

83 Ernst Von Meyer, History of Chemistry (New York: MacMillan Company, 1891) p. 169.

84 F. K. Richtmyer, Introduction to Modern Physics (New York: McGraw-Hill Company, 1934) p. 66.

85 H. Rouse and S. Ince, History of Hydraulics (Iowa City, Iowa: Iowa State University, 1957) p. 135.

86 A. E. Love, Mathematical Theory of Elasticity (New York: Dover Publications, 1944) p. 9.

87 James K. Finch, Trends in Engineering Education (New York: Columbia University Press, 1948) p. 11.

Engineering Practice in Early 19th Century

Manufacturing.—One of the major engineering concerns in America at the time of the revolution and for a period immediately following was the need for the development of manufacturing. Clothing, food, military equipment, tools, and other supplies no longer available from England due to the non-importation agreement of 1774 had to be supplied.[88] Following the war, England sought to injure the American industries by dumping. The threat of an industrial domination comparable to the previous political one was a serious danger. Mann states the British attitude and the American reaction as follows:

> After the war England sought to crush the incipient American industries by selling her goods here at lower prices than were charged at home. The Confederation was threatened by an industrial domination that seemed no less oppressive than political domination. This crisis was met, first, by the formation of numerous societies for the promotion of the useful arts, to encourage a spirit of inquiry, industry, and experiment among the members; second, by offering premiums from state treasuries for such improvements in the useful arts as might seem beneficial to the country; and third, by inviting trained artisans from abroad to settle here and give America the benefit of their training.[89]

The American solutions mentioned by Mann contain many recommendations advanced by Alexander Hamilton. Hamilton, in a comprehensive plan for stimulating industry and commerce, stressed pecuniary bounties, premiums, and exemption of duty on the raw materials of manufacture.[90] John Adams included these same elements in the 1780 Constitution of Massachusetts, of which he was the principal author. As is evident from the following extract, provisions for supporting colleges and schools were also included.

> Wisdom and knowledge, as well as virtue, diffused generally among the bodies of the people, being necessary for the preservation of their rights and liberties; and as these depend on spreading the opportunities and advantages of education in the various parts of the country, and among the different orders of the people, it shall be the duty of legislatures and magistrates, in all future providences of the commonwealth, to cherish the interests of literature and the sciences, and all seminaries of them; especially the universty at Cambridge, public schools, and grammar schools in the towns; to encourage private societies and public institutions, rewards, and immunities for the promotion of agriculture, arts,

[88] Howard R. Smith, *Economic History of the United States* (New York: The Ronald Press, 1955) p. 58.

[89] Charles R. Mann, *A Study of Engineering Education,* Bulletin Carnegie Foundation for Foundation for Advancement of Teaching, 1918-20 (No. 11; Boston: Merrymount Press) p. 3.

[90] Henry C. Lodge, *The Works of Alexander Hamilton* (Vol. 4; New York: G. P. Putnam and Company, 1905) p. 152.

sciences, commerce, trades, manufactures, and national history of the country.[91]

The societies referred to were not new to the colonies, and in general were of three types.

One such society was established in Boston in 1751 as the "Society for Encouraging Industry and Employing the Poor," and as the name indicates, was primarily a public welfare organization."[92] A second type, founded in 1775 in Philadelphia, was more of a financial venture and was termed, "The United Company of Philadelphia for Promotion of American Manufactures," with the members owning shares in units of ten pounds each..[93] The third form of society or organization was a labor group and is described by Beard in the following:

> During the quarter of a century that followed the inauguration of Washington as first President of the United States in 1789, the skilled workmen of the American towns formed powerful local organizations to take part in the fixing of wages, hours and the conditions of the industries generally.—The printers carried on their own affairs and the shoemakers theirs.[94]

It was within the above political industrial framework that our first engineers devoted to manufacturing operated. These men for the most part were self taught and succeeded in accomplishing some great engineering in the face of an inadequate and often erroneous statement of basic theory. Under such conditions many of the great inventions of our times came into being without the benefit of science, and often in spite of the predictions of eminent scientists.[95] To illustrate how the various methods operated in encouraging industry a few cases will be cited.

> *John Litch* (1743-1798). — Litch, who learned his trade as a clock maker and foundry worker, turned his attention to the invention of a steam boat from 1785 to his death. After failing to secure subsidies from the Continental Congress and several scientific societies, he turned to the state legislatures, and from New Jersey in 1786, and in 1787 from Pennsyvania, New York, Delaware, and Virginia, he obtained the exclusive privilege for fourteen years of building and operating steam boats on all waters of these several states.[96]
>
> *Samuel Slater* (1768-1835). — In discussing manufacturing, Wright

91 F. N. Thorpe, *American Charters Constitutions and Organic Laws* 1892 (Vol. 3;Washington , D. C.: Government Printing Office, 1909) p. 1907.

92 Victor S. Clark, *History of Manufactures in the United States,* CarnegieInstitution of Washington (New York: NewYork Lithographing Corp., 1929) p. 183.

93 *Ibid.,* p. 183.

94 Mary R. Beard, *The American Labor Movement* (New York: Macmillian Company 1942) p. 17.

95 Gordon S. Brown, "The Modern Engineer Should be Educated as a Scientist," *Journal of Engineering Education* (Vol. 43; Dec. 1952) p. 274.

96 "John Litch,"*Dictionary of American Biography* (Vol. 10, 1936) p. 91.

makes the following statements: A start was made in 1790, when Samuel Slater, attracted to the country by the rewards offered for improved cotton machinery, set up an Arkwright mill for spinning cotton at Pawtucket, Rhode Island. This relieved the difficulty in the industry due to the scarcity of yarn, and the success of this mill soon led to the erection of others; so that, despite numerous failures, there were about 70 such water power mills in the country in 1810, mostly located in southern New England.[97]

Eli Whitney (1765-1825).—Eli Whitney invented the cotton gin and developed interchangeable parts in making guns for the government. The following statement describing, in part, his experiences with the state of South Carolina, illustrates still further the payment of money by the state for industrial improvements: "They closed their session at 10 o'clock last evening. A few hours previous to their breaking up they voted fifty thousand dollars to purchase my patent right to the Machine for Cleaning Cotton, 20 thousand of which is to be paid in hand and the rest in three equal annual payments of 10 thousand Dollars each."[98]

Although Whitney felt he was underpaid, not all were as fortunate as he. Oliver Evans (1755-1819), who made the first machinery for flour mills, was refused financial assistance by the Pennsylvania legislature.[99] Nickolas Roosevelt, who built the equipment for the Philadelphia water works, applied to both Pennsylvania and Maryland for grants for some of his contributions; Pennsylvania gave him grants for some of his work and Maryland allowed for all.

Road Building.—Few roads were constructed in America prior to the revolution, and these were not the work of engineers. Most early settlers were located along bays or rivers and transportation was generally by water. After the war, public demand led to the improvement of various roads by private enterprise. These improvements generally took the form of toll roads or "turnpikes" and were principally used to connect large cities.[100] One of the early toll roads was the Philadelphia-Lancaster Turnpike, which was 62 miles long and surfaced to a width of 24 feet with hand broken stone and gravel. This road has been attributed to be the result of the Whiskey Rebellion of 1794. The farmers objected to the tax on the whiskey they were making from their grain; their contention was that they were forced to make whiskey, as a pack horse could carry only four baskets of grain over the mountains, but in the form of whiskey he could carry the product of twenty-four bushels.[101]

[97] Chester W. Wright, *Economic History of the United States* (New York:McGraw-Hill Book Company, 1949) p. 223.

[98] Jeannette Mersky and Allan Nevins, *op. cit.,* p. 152.

[99] Coleman Setlers, *Oliver Evans and His Inventions,* Journal of the Franklin Institute, 1886.

[100] L. J. Ritter and R. J. Paquette, *Highway Engineering,* (New York: The Ronald Press Company, 1951) p. 5.

[101] L. D. Hewes and C. H. Oglesby, *Highway Engineering* (New York: John Wiley and Sons, 1954) p. 4.

In the building of this road the state, for the first time in America, exercised its power of eminent domain to aid private capital. There were many applicants for the stock, which earned from six to fifteen percent; the cost of construction proved to be about $7,000 a mile. Matthias Slough, one of the contractors, resented the implication that costs were too high and protested "I can lay my hand on my heart, and declare that I, in no instance, wontedly, sported with one shilling of the Company's money."[102]

In 1806, the first road that was originally toll-free and financed by the Federal Government was started. It was the "Old National Pike" or "Cumberland Road" from Cumberland, Maryland to Wheeling, West Virginia. It took ten years to construct this section. Later it was extended to Columbus, Ohio and St. Louis, Missouri.

Canal Building.—Early canal building in this country was the product of the vision of early explorers, of the experience of the English canal builders, and of the need, before the advent of the railroad, for expanded water navigation to supplement road development.

Louis Joliet, exploring the wilderness with Father Marquette in 1673, pointed out that a water connection between Lake Michigan and the Illinois River might easily be achieved. This would make it possible to go from Lake Michigan to Florida by the aid of one canal cutting only over one-half league of prairie. La Salle also mentioned the desirability of such a canal; and in 1795 the Indians were induced to grant a right-of-way through their land for it.[103] Harlow also mentions that the Cape Cod Canal in Massachusetts was suggested as early as 1697 and in 1776 a special committee was appointed to make an investigation.

Private corporations built many of the canals, such as the one at Charleston, South Carolina. The company was chartered in 1786. The canal was 22 miles long, 35 feet wide at the surface and 4 feet deep. The work was mostly done by slave labor and took seven years to complete.

The canals were, for the most part, built by American engineers, who had no special training for the work. One of these men, James Geddes (1763-1838) had only an elementary education but constructed many of the canals in Ohio, Pennsylvania, Maine, and New York. One of the outstanding engineers was imported from England. This man, William Weston (1752-1833), was contracted to complete a canal already started by the Schuykill and Susquehanna Navigation Company. He arrived in America in 1793 and stayed for seven years before returning to England. He was hired independently by the elder Loammi Baldwin to work on a Massachusetts canal and by George Washington to report on the locks under construction at the great falls of the

---

[102] John T. Faris, *Old Roads Out of Philadelphia* (Philadelphia: J. B. Lippincott Company, 1927) p. 114.

[103] Alvin F. Harlow, *Old Towpath* (New York: D. Appleton and Company, 1926) p. 5.

Potomac River. For his first assignment he recived 800 pounds for seven months service, and was offered $7,000 to become chief engineer of the Erie Canal.

By 1830, there were 1,277 miles of canals in America, located in the states of New York, Pennsylvania, and Ohio.[104] From the point of view of engineering education the following statement is significant:

> Possiblly no one among the American engineers who worked on the Erie Canal had even seen a canal dug before. Some familiarized themselves with British practice, as did White, or studied the Middlesex Canal in Massachusetts; all learned in the training school of experience. From the Erie, many went to other canals and on into the new, though not too dissimilar, profession of railroad building. Their achievements on the Erie Canal, while worthy of note, should not be overstressed. The fact persists, despite legend, that the engineering of the Erie Canal, though effective, was neither especially difficult nor unique.[105]

Bridge Building.—Intimately connected with both road and canal building was bridge building. Arch bridges of stone had been successfully built since the time of the Romans. In 1763 Perronnet of the French Department des Ponts et Chaussees simplified the pier construction of arch bridges by the use of applied mechanics. For the most part, however, bridge designs prior to 1800 and for many years afterwards were almost entirely empirical.[106]

The engineers, including Louis Wernwag (1769-1843) who was famous for the 27 wooden bridges he designed in his active career of 27 years, were men without formal technical education.[107] Despite this apparent handicap, America soon caught up with England in the regard to bridge design. Not only were arch, truss, and suspension bridges constructed; but stone, cast iron, wrought iron, and wood were all utilized. Some of the accomplishments of the self-made engineers include a two-span bridge in 1792 by Colonel Enoch Hale with each span 175 feet lang; a 100-foot-span bridge by Timothy Palmer in 1792; a 320-foot-span by Louis Wernwag in 1812; and a 244-foot center-to-center suspension bridge by James Finley in 1801.[108] Ithiel Town invented the so-called "Town Truss" in 1820 and Thomas Pope wrote a treatise on bridge architecture in 1811.

[104] G. R. Tayler, *The Transportation Revolution* (New York: Rinehart and Company, 1951) p. 79.
[105] Richard Shelton Kirby, et. al., *Engineering in History* (New York: McGraw Hill Company, 1956) p. 218.
[106] H. Merriman and H. S. Jacoby, *Roofs and Bridges* (New York: John Wiley and Sons, 1905) p. 5.
[107] John Wernwag, "Letter to Samuel Smedly" *Engineering News* (Oct. 15, 1885) p. 99.
[108] P. S. Laurson, "Development of Bridge Construction," *Journal of Engineering Education* (Vol. 38; 1930) p. 453.

chapter **3**

The Formative Stage in American Engineering Education (1800-1835)

Introductory Considerations

During the period from 1800 to 1835, the United States purchased Louisiana in 1803, engaged in the War of 1812 with England, had a depression and purchased Florida in 1819. Following the War of 1812 the Northwest Territory was rapidly settled and from it was carved the states of Ohio, Indiana, Michigan, Illinois and Wisconsin.[1] This territorial acquisition and expansion was accompanied by an increase in population from 5,308,483 in 1800 to 12,664,627 in 1830. This population remained predominantly rural, with the percentage of urban population increasing from 6.05 to 8.9 during this thirty year period.[2]

The problems of education were complex, and of these engineering education was but one part. On the secondary level the Latin school with its restricted curriculum and limited enrollment was, at the beginning of the century, still common but was gradually being supplemented by the academy as the period evolved. The public high school was just making its beginning with the establishment of the Boston English High School in 1821. The number of colleges of the traditional classical type increased during the period. The United States Military Academy at West Point followed the original French tradition of combining training of military engineers and civil engineers in one institution.

The need for trained engineers was everywhere apparent as the mileage of canals increased to 1,277 in 1830 and to 3,326 in 1840.[3] In addition, public roads increased from 1,200 miles in 1800 to 47,562 in 1835,[4] while the

---

[1] J. Craf, *Economic Development of the United States* (New York: McGraw-Hill Book Company) p. 310.
[2] *Historical Statistics of the United States 1789-1945, Bureau of Census*, Department of Commerce, Washington, D.C.
[3] G. R. Tayler, *The Transportation Revolution* (New York: Reinhart & Co., 1955), p. 79.
[4] *Ibid.*, p. 220.

31

railroad movement started, with 1,098 miles being constructed by 1835.[5] In the industrial field there was the screw propeller invented by Stevens in 1804, the steamboat by Fulton in 1807, the reaper by McCormick in 1834, the revolver by Colt and the electric telegraph by Morse in 1835.[6] In addition, facilities for making iron products were being developed. The Americans had since 1750 been encouraged by the English to supply pig iron but had been discouraged from making finished iron products.[7]

The purpose of this chapter is to supply some of the information as to how engineering education had its beginning in this setting. It will be indicated how engineering education was intimately tied up with agriculture, teacher training, military training, state support, and European tradition. The background of the leaders in this field will be presented to indicate the type of citizen who saw the need and sought in various ways to contribute to this formative stage in American engineering education.

United States Military Academy

Considerations as First Engineering School.—When the United States Military Academy was officially established at West Point in 1802, it was expected that the institution would supply the country with engineers for civil as well as military purposes. This idea is reflected by James McHenry, who as secretary of war in 1800, wrote to John Adams defining the duties of the United States Engineer Corps:

> We must not conclude that the services of the engineer is limited to fortifications. This is but a single branch of the profession; their ability extends to almost every department of war; besides embracing whatever respects public building, roads, canals, and all such work of a civil nature.[8]

A little later, in 1809, Thomas Jefferson stated in a special message to the Senate and the House of Representatives:

> The scale on which the military academy at West Point was originally established, is becoming too limited to furnish the number of well instructed subjects in the different branches of artillery and engineering which the public service calls for.[9]

In keeping with these early purposes, West Point for the complete period prior to the civil war served in the dual capacity of a school for training offi-

[5] *Ibid.,* p. 300.
[6] S. Chase, *Men and Machines* (New York: Macmillan Co., 1929) p. 78.
[7] B. Hindle, *The Pursuit of Science in Revolutionary America* (Chapel Hill: University of North Carolina Press, 1956) p. 207.
[8] "Engineering Education," *Transaction of American Society of Civil Engineers* (Vol. 54; Part A; New York: The Society) p. 456.
[9] Andrew Lipencomb (ed.) *The Writings of Thomas Jefferson* (Vol. 3;Washington D.C.: Thomas Jefferson Memorial Association, 1904) p. 471.

cers and a national school of civil engineering. From the point of view of technical education in America it was the only school of civil engineering until 1835. A large proportion of the important engineering positions prior to 1850 were filled by graduates of West Point. General Cullum shows that the 150 West Point graduates practicing civil engineering prior to 1840 were a very important fraction of all the civil engineers in service.[10] Of this group at least 30 percent had distinguished careers as chief engineers of important railways, canals, or other public works. This percentage was arrived at by Wellington, who reviewed the biographies of the complete number of 150 as given by Cullum.[11] It is on the basis of such facts as these that West Point had often been termed the first engineering school in America. Regardless of the classification, the Academy's influence was important, and a more detailed study of its formation and operation as contributing to engineering education in America is warranted.

The Founding of West Point.—The question of a national military academy was debated by the cabinet in November, 1793. Washington, Randolph, Knox, and Hamilton favored its establishment; but Thomas Jefferson doubted whether such an act would be constitutional. Owing to the threats of war Congress did not act on the basic issue, but as an immediate measure passed the act of May 7, 1794. This act authorized the recruitment of a Corps of Artillerists and Engineers and assigned them to the garrison at West Point. A rank of cadet was also created, and it was expected that these cadets and junior officers would attend regular classes, for which books and apparatus were provided.[12] As there were no engineers in the army to carry on the construction program contemplated by the corps, President Washington made temporary appointments of men of foreign birth to superivse the work.[13]

Four years after its organization, President Adams in 1798 was authorized to appoint four teachers in the arts and sciences to instruct the artillerists and engineers. The Secretary of War (Dexter) received a letter from President Adams stating:

> He [the President] is ready to appoint 64 cadets, 4 teachers and 2 engineers; he directs that books and instruments should be bought; is of the opinion that cadets should be instructed at different stations in rotation; that mid-shipmen should be admitted also; and he asks if Captain W. A. Barron and Mr. B. de Pusy will do as teachers.[14]

[10] George W. Cullum, *Biographical Register of Officers and Graduates of the United States Military Academy* (Vol. 3; Boston: Houghton Mifflin Co, 1891) p. 2300.
[11] A. M. Wellington, "The Engineering Schools of the United States III" *Engineering News,* (Vol 27; April 2, 1892) p. 318.
[12] Sidney Forman, *West Point* (New York: Columbia University Press, 1950) p. 14.
[13] L. D. Ingersoll, *A History of the War Department of the United States* (Washington, D. C.: Francis B. Mohum Company, 1879) p. 34.
[14] *Centennial of the United States Military Academy* (Vol. 1; Washington, D. C.: Government Printing Office, 1904) p. 219.

The President appointed George Baron and Captain W. A. Barron to teaching positions. Mr. Baron had been an instructor at the British Military Academy at Woolwich. He stayed at West Point but 13 months, as his civilian status gave him little authority to enforce English methods at West Point. It is apparent that President Adams was anxious to have a military academy established, and with this in mind he had cast around for a likely superintendent to head the proposed institution. It is a curious fact that Adams offered the position of superintendent of West Point to Count Rumford. The offer was made through Ambassador Rufus King in London but was not accepted. From the point of view of professional qualifications, the Count ranked very high due to his experiments in artillery, heat, and chemistry, together with his experience in establishing a military school in Bavaria, for which he was made a count. On the other hand, Count Rumford was the Benjamin Thompson who had studied under John Winthrop at Harvard. Due to his associations at the time of the Revolutionary War he was branded as a Royalist and saw fit to leave America and join forces with the British during the Revolution. He never again returned to America, although he did endow a professorship at Harvard upon his death.

In the spring of 1801, Thomas Jefferson took office as President; one of his first acts was to take practical steps leading to the esablishment of the United States Military Academy. This action is of interest because it was Jefferson who in 1793 had questioned the constitutionality of its being established. At that time he was the only member of the cabinet who was for looking into the matter further rather than for acting on Washington's desire for its immediate establishment.

The work of Jefferson moved ahead and on March 16, 1802 the organic act establishing the United States Military Academy was passed by Congress. The pertinent sections of the law read as follows:

Sec. 26. And be it further enacted, That the President of the United States is hereby authorized and empowered, when he shall deem it expedient, to organize and establish a corps of engineers, to consist of one engineer, with the pay, rank and emoluments of a major; two assistant engineers, with the pay, rank and emoluments of captains; two other assistant engineers with the pay, rank, and emoluments of first Lieutenants; two other assistant engineers, with the pay, rank, and emoluments of second lieutenants; and ten cadets with the pay of sixteen dollars per month, and two rations per day; and the President of the United States is, in like manner, authorized when he shall deem it proper, to make such promotions in the said corps, with a view to particular merit, and without regard to rank, not to exceed one colonel, one lieutenant-colonel, two majors, four captains, four first-lieutenants, and so that the number of the whole corps shall at no time, exceed twenty officers and cadets.

Sec. 27. And be it further enacted, That the said corps when so organized shall be stationed at West Point, in the State of New York, and shall constitute a military academy; and the engineers and assistant engineers, and cadets of the said Corps, shall be subject at all times to do duty in such places, and on such services, as the President of the United States shall direct.

Sec. 28. And be it further enacted, That the principal engineer, and in his absence the next in rank, shall have the superintendence of the said Academy under the direction of the President of the United States; and the Secretary of War is hereby authorized, at the public expense, under such regulations as should be directed, to buy the books, implements and apparatus for the use and benefit of the said institution.[15]

West Point 1802-1812.—In 1801 President Jefferson appointed Jonathan Williams inspector of fortifications and superintendent of the military post at West Point. Williams was known to Jefferson as the grandnephew of Benjamin Franklin and the translator, from French to English, of a treatise on artillery. Williams' education was adequate and consisted of four years at Harvard and fifteen years of private study in business and science under the direction of his uncle. Some of the results of the work he produced, while living with Franklin in Europe from 1770 to 1785, were published in the Transaction of the American Philosophical Society.

A year after his appointment a new act was passed specifying the ranking engineer as superintendent of the Military Academy at West Point. This practice of having an engineer superintendent of West Point continued from its founding in 1802 to 1866.[16] This dual position posed difficulties, and Williams found that his duties as ranking officer of the army engineers conflicted with his position of superintendent of the academy. The position of chief of the army engineers necessitated his being frequently away from West Point, to inspect army projects and to direct the construction work connected with the defense of New York Harbor. In addition to this handicap, Williams had to work under the Secretary of War, William Eustis, who was antagonistic toward West Point. Eustis made Williams' position uncomfortable by withholding supplies and seeing to it that new appointments were not made when vacancies occurred.[17] In the face of these difficulties Williams initiated some practical experiments on war equipment. This work was practically successful and resulted in an act of 1803 authorizing him to enlist, for a term of not less than three years, one artificer and eighteen men to aid in making practical experiments. This act was considered inadequate by Williams and resulted in his resignation that same year. Even though the Academy cannot be said to have prospered under his administration, he was approached and persuaded to accept a reappointment in 1805 with the rank of Lieutenant Colonel.

[15] Sidney Forman, *op. cit.*, p. 18-19.
[16] Centennial of the United States Military Academy, op., p. 235.
[17] *Ibid.*, p. 32.

Upon his reappointment he suggested that the Academy be moved to Washington, with the authority of its operation placed directly under the President of the United States. Jefferson was in agreement with this change but no action was ever taken on the matter. Realizing that no change was to be made in the location of the Academy, Williams sought to offset the geographical isolation by organizing the Military Philosophical Society.[18] Although the Corps of Engineers, including the cadets, was the nucleus of the organization, many distinguished people outside of the military service belonged. This outside group included such people as Thomas Jefferson, James Madison, John Q. Adams, James Monroe, John Marshall, De Witt Clinton, Robert Fulton, Eli Whitney, and Clement Biddle. This activity transformed West Point into a national center of scientific study as subjects outside the curriculum were explored.

During this first ten year period of operation there was no consistent system of instruction or examination in use. The cadets were not arranged in distinct classes, and definite courses of study were not prescribed. Some of the cadets were married and other single, with their ages varying from twelve to twenty-four years. The lower age was not an unusual practice for the colleges of the day. At Princeton in the year 1825 it is reported that youths seeking admission were often only thirteen or fourteen years of age, and most of them went into the sophomore class.[19] Students entered any time of the year without examination and were often without uniforms. By 1812 only eighty-nine cadets had been graduated.[20] Of this number approximately one-fifth were classified as engineers.

Although the appointment of 156 cadets was authorized in 1808, the greatest number in attendance at any one time up to 1812 was 36; the average did not exceed 20.[21]

The instruction in military engineering for this same period was by lectures delivered by the superintendent. These lectures were illustrated by a model of a fortification and by field exercises in practical engineering. The only text book used was a small pamphlet of fifty pages translated from the French by Jonathan Williams.[22] The course in drawing was very elementary in character and confined to topography and fortification drawing. The method of instruction was essentially that of copying other drawings. The mathematics taught was based on Hutton's "Compendium of Mathematics," and included arithmetic, logarithms, algebra, trigonometry, land surveying, and

[18] S. Foreman, "The United States Military Philosophical Academy 1802-1812."*The William and Mary Quarterly* (July, 1954).
[19] Thomas J. Wertenbaker, *op. cit.,*p. 161.
[20] *The Sesquicentennial of the United States Military Academy* (Buffalo, New York; Baker, Jones, Hausauer, and Saverage, Inc., 1953) p. 13.
[21] A. M. Wellington, *op. cit.,* p. 343.
[22] Centennial of the United States Military Academy, *op. cit.,* p. 277.

conics. As in the colleges of the day, some natural philosophy was taught.

In 1812 when the war with England broke out, Williams resigned and the Academy practically ceased to exist. In this same year the Academy Board, by a statement using the words, "when any cadet shall receive a regular degree from the academic staff,"[23] was given the authority to confer degrees. This implied a privilege that was not utilized at the time. Degrees were not conferred until 1933, when the degree of Bachelor of Science was specifically authorized.[24] The entrance requirement of 1812, providing that each candidate should be well versed in reading, writing, and arithmeic, remained in force until 1866. Another change in 1812 was increasing to 250 the number of cadets that might be appointed. To take care of this proposed increase, professorships in mathematics, engineering, and natural philosophy were created. Alden Patridge, who later founded Norwich University, was appointed one of these professors. All the reforms cited were necessary, as up to this time the offerings of the Academy varied in only two respects from the college of that day. These differences were the lack of classical language and the addition of the practical approach as manifested by field work, demonstrations and inspection trips.

Thayer's West Point (1817-1833).—Following the war of 1812 West Point was on a stronger basis than ever before. In 1817 Sylvanus Thayer (1785-1872) was appointed superintendent by President Monroe, who had previously, as Secretary of War, commissioned him to study military and technical developments in France. In addition to his European training, Thayer had graduated from Dartmouth College in 1807 and from the Military Academy in 1808.

At the time of the appointment there were approximately 400 people under his command, of whom 240 were cadets and 15 were professors and teachers. Thayer immediately initiated many reforms which involved arranging cadets into four annual classes. He divided the classes into small sections, requiring weekly class reports; developed a scale of marks, and directed more thorough recitations. Weights were attached to subjects giving their relative value on the curriculum. For the year 1820 the total points of the complete curriculum were 10.5, distributed as follows: engineering 2, natural philosophy 2, mathematics 2, drawing 1, French 5, tactics 1, conduct 1, and geography-history 1. By making these changes Thayer transformed the Military Academy from a more or less elementary school to one that set the pattern for much of our technical education in America.

The teaching was based on French texts used at the Ecole Polytechnique and on others written in this country or translated from the French. Mathematics was extended to include both differential calculus and integral calculus.

[23] *Ibid.*, p. 226.
[24] Sidney Forman, *op. cit.*, p. 199.

The course in civil engineering was considerably strengthened, especially after 1832, when Dennis Mahan, an Academy graduate of the class of 1824, was appointed to the staff. Mahan, like Thayer, had studied in Europe. In addition to his teaching, Mahan developed a complete set of textbooks. His courses included bridge design and problems associated with the design and construction of roads, canals, and railroads.

The above courses had immediate application, as many of the graduates directed civilian work that was then in progress. An example of this practice was the design, layout, and construction of the Baltimore and Ohio Railroad. When the company asked for technical assistance from the Government, several army officers were assigned to aid them, and the company's reports on their contributions were extremely favorable.[25] This practice was responsible for many of the changes in the curriculum and affected the future careers of many of the cadets. In fact some of the cadets attended the Academy for the sole purpose of training for civilian practice, which paid many of the graduates from $5,000 to $16,000 per year.[26] To attach some relative value to this amount it may be noted that college presidents during this period were receiving but $1,500 and resident professors but $1,000, with the student paying $36 a year tuition.[27]

For the total period from its formal establishment in 1802 to 1827 the total number graduated from the Academy was 500, which included 121 engineers. Of these engineers, 57 became civil engineers engaged in private work and 64 entered the corps of engineering of the United States Army.[28] This number was not sufficient to supervise and design the many engineering works then under construction. A good example of this was the Erie Canal, which was engineered by James Geddes, Benjamin Wright, and Charles Brodhead who were all lacking in formal engineering training.[29] This natural talent, characteristic of the period, is described by Ashbel Welch as follows:

> Many of the distinctive characteristics of American engineering originated with those Erie Canal engineers. We practice their method today, though most of their very names are forgotten. As a class, they wrote little. There were then no engineering papers prepared, and no engineering societies to perpetuate them if they had been prepared. They were not scientific men, but knew by calculation. Judge Wright's counsel was 'as if a man had inquired at the oracle of God.' What science they had, they knew well how to apply to the best advantage. Few men have ever accomplished so much with so little means.[30]

[25] Sidney Forman, op. cit., p. 77.
[26] Ibid., p. 85.
[27] W. C. Bronson, op. cit., p. 231.
[28] A. M. Wellington, op. cit., p. 318.
[29] D. Fitzgerald, Early Enginnering Work in the United States, Vol. DV. Transactions of the American Society of Civil Engineers, 1899, p. 596.
[30] Ashbel Welch, Transactions of the American Society of Civil Engineers (Published by the Society, 1882) Vo. 11, p. 168

The above information is given to indicate that the contributions of West Point were not sufficient for the needs of the time. The young American States embarked on many important engineering ventures under the leadership of men trained under the pupilage system. The pupilage system was accepted to such an extent that the Erie Canal is frequently referred to as the first American Engineering University, and the Baltimore and Ohio Railroad as the first school of railroad engineering in the United States.[31] Formal technical and engineering education was definitely needed, however, and a description of some of the early attempts to establish such institutions are essential to the development of this study.

Pioneer Proposals for Establishing Technical Schools

Educational Pattern of Early 19th Century.—With the newborn states depending upon their own economic and intellectual resources, it was evident that the existing educational program was inadequate. The Latin grammar school, with its emphasis on the classical languages, was just beginning to be replaced by the tuition academy. Public secondary education was very limited. As late as 1830 there were only seven high schools [32] and 950 academies[33] in the United States. From the beginning of the century to 1830 the number of liberal arts colleges increased from 24 to 90 in number. The persistent demand for technical training was given little attention and the attempts to establish a new type of institution with new kinds of teachers made but little progress. In the main, the few attempts to inaugurate technical education were entirely outside of the engineering profession. The advances made were accomplished by individuals who saw the necessity for a change in the educational program if America was to maintain its democratic spirit and become economically self sufficient.

Early Efforts of Thomas Jefferson.—Prior to the chartering of the University of Virginia in 1819 and its opening in 1825 Thomas Jefferson had proposed a state school in 1814. His plan for this institution was rather detailed and was contained in a letter he wrote on September 7, 1814 to Peter Carr.[34] In this letter he states:

> I have very long entertained the hope that this our native state, would take up the subject of education and make an establishment, either with or without incorporation into that of William and Mary, where every branch of science, deemed useful at this day, should be taught in its highest degree.

[31] J. K. Finch, *Trends in Engineering Education* (New York: Columbia University Press, 1948) p. 11.
[32] E. G. Dexter, *A History of Education in the United States* (New York: Macmillan Company, 1904) p. 173.
[33] E. P. Cubberly, *op. cit.,* p. 69.
[34] A. A. Lipscomp (ed.) *op. cit.,* (Vol. 19) p. 211.

To accomplish this task he proposed four professorships: one each in Languages, Mathematics and Physics, Chemistry, and Zoology, and in Philosophy. This academy, or college as it was termed, had its trustees already selected at the time of Jefferson's letter. Although the school was never established, the project was indicative of the need, and in this particular case contained many of the proposals that were incorporated into the University of Virginia by Jefferson at a later date.

Governor Brown's Ohio Proposal. — On January 8, 1819, Governor Brown of Ohio proposed the establishment of a state polytechnic school which in many of its provisions was ahead of its time. The recommendations were embodied in a general message to the legislature emphasizing the social importance of education and concerning itself with education on all levels. The portion of the message specifically having to do with the creation of a state polytechnic school reads as follows:

> It is understood that a resolution is now before the legislature for appointing two persons, one a mineralogist and chemist, and the other a civil engineer, to be employed upon state establishment. (Here follows a rather lengthy discussion of the value of the services these two functionaries could render in surveying the mineral resources of the state, planning highways and bridges, etc., and especially in advising the Legislature as to the practicability of a system of canals.)
>
> Some of these observations may be thought digressive to the main purpose of this communication, namely education: but they are connected in this; that it appears practicable, should the Legislature think proper to employ these two characters, to render them doubly useful by making them professor, and principal instructors in a polytechnic school; under the immediate patronage and care of the state; for instruction in the theoretical and scientific principles of the most useful arts.
>
> Without wishing to derogate from the pleasure and real utility of classical and polite literature; or prevent the study of the works of the ancients, in their own language, which the taste of the student shall prompt, or his means enable him to pursue; permit me to observe that there is a description of science, constantly required, by persons in the industrious walks of life, who cannot afford the time and expense of, what is usually called, a liberal education.
>
> The proposed institution may be viewed, as a fountain, where the young artist may imbibe a higher relish for his trade, and an energy in practice, resulting from a conscious safety in his experiments, tested by a familiar acquaintance with the natural laws and principles that govern the object of his pursuits. This idea is suggested, not only for the assistance of the aspiring workman, laboring under a fundamental ignorance of this part of his profession, but with a further view to the discovery and use, of many sources of individual and public advantage. There is some reason to hope that such an establishment would be influential, in causing agriculture, and the most necessary arts to be followed with more skill and assiduity, by rendering them more safe and lucrative;

and you would manifestly increase the disposition of our inhabitants to embrace those beneficial occupations by giving them the consideration justly their due in a republic, where the most useful ought to be considered the most honorable employments. This I presume would be effected in no small degree by causing them to be considered the objects of scientific as well as laborious pursuit.

To add incentive to the virtue of industry, by giving dignity to its exertion, and yielding to a meritorious and useful enterprise, would be a work worthy of your labors.

If the public revenue, after defraying other necesary expenses, shall be deemed insufficient, to cover the additional charge of the professorships, it is thought that a light tax, specifically applicable to these objects, and fairly graduated, on iron works, mills, canals, and locks, without being bundensome would produce an immediate income of several thousand dollars and with the continual addition to those works would be of increasing productiveness. It is also presumed, that as the effect is likely to operate with immediate benefit of those establishments; it would be paid with cheerfulness.

It would be a reasonable hope that Congress, in consideration of procuring an enhanced price for the public lands by reason of the formation of canals; may be induced to yield assistance in furthering the design .

I cannot nor do I wish to conceal my desire of participating with the legislature, in the glory of laying the foundation of permanent establishments, that shall give additional prosperity to our state, and luster to its name; and could have not be undertaken as I hope, I should reflect with pride, that they were commenced during my administration.[35]

The recommendations contained in the above message are remarkable in as much as they anticipated many of the later views and practices. The idea that a school would enhance the prosperity of the state by an intelligent exploration of its natural resources was an advanced concept; as was the providing of off-campus services by specialists in the persons of the mineralogist and the civil engineer. In considering the time when Ethan Brown made this proposal, it may be noted that it was not until six years later, in 1825, that the state of Ohio created a state system of elementary education. This may account for the fact that the resolution calling for the appointment of a mineralogist and a civil engineer did not pass the house, and Brown's proposal for the creation of the polytechnic school was not acted upon. It is well to note that the idea of a state creating and supporting an institution of higher education was relatively new, though the practice of making grants to private colleges was not. An example of state support by special grant is illustrated by an act of the Massachusetts legislature in 1814, when it appropriated to Harvard, Bowdoin, and Williams colleges for ten years, the proceeds of a bank tax.[36]

[35] R. H. Eckelberry, *An Early Proposal for a State Polytechnic School*, Ohio Archaeological and Historical Quarterly (Columbus, Ohio: Published by the Society, 1930) p. 501-402.

[36] S. E. Morison, *op. cit.*, p. 214.

Buel's New York State Proposal.—Jesse Buel (1778-1839), a printer, publisher, agriculturalist, and legislator, became interested in scientific agriculture to the extent of operating a model farm in 1822. He held the position of secretary of the New York State Board of Agriculture and edited three volumes published by this body during its six years of existence. When he was elected from the Albany County to the New York State Assembly in 1823, Buel became the leading spokesman for agriculture.[37]

In March of 1823, he presented a report and offered a resolution urging the establishment of a tax supported school of agriculture along the lines that had proved so successful at the Fellenberg School in Switzerland.[38] He gave full details of the plan, the method to be used, and the results to be expected. What is of particular importance is that one of the final statements of the proposal promised that if the state would undertake the support of the school the Honorable Stephen Van Rensselaer would donate the necessary land. In view of what later developed it is difficult to determine the motive behind the apparent generosity of Van Rensselaer. Buel's efforts on behalf of the agricultural education failed, but finally in 1835, under the pressure of an agricultural convention, he caused the legislature to act—albeit in rather weak fashion. The legislature created a school to be financed by money to be raised by public subscription rather than by state appropriation. As a result of this action Buel and his supporters became discouraged and no school was established.

The American Literary Scientific and Military Academy

(Norwich University)

Captain Alden Partridge.—Alden Partridge, who established the American Literary, Scientific, and Military Academy at Norwich Vermont in 1819, was born in 1785 and attended Dartmouth College from 1802 to 1805. In 1805 he received an appointment to West Point and graduated a year later with the class of 1806. Upon graduation, he continued on at the Academy in various positions from the date of his graduation to 1817. He was first assistant professor of mathematics and then a professor of civil engineering. From 1808 to 1815 he acted as superintendent for brief intervals owing to the frequent absences of Colonel Williams from the post. For two years, 1815 to 1817, he was the official superintendent of the Academy.[39]

The career of Alden Partridge at West Point was anything but smooth. He placed members of his family in various position of authority. As a drill master and teacher he served well, but as superintendent and administrator

[37] "Jesse Buel" *Dictionary of American Biography* (Vol. 3, 1938) p. 238.
[38] Mann, *op. cit.*, p. 4.
[39] G. M. Dodge, and W. A. Ellis, *Norwich University* 1819-1911 (Montpelier, Vermont, 1911; Vol. 2) p. 22.

his faulty judgments and domineering nature contributed to his final displacement.[40] When Thayer was appointed superintendent, Partridge returned to the post without official orders and arbitrarily assumed command. For this act, he was court martialed and found guilty of several charges, a fact which resulted in his dismissal from the service. In consideration of his previous work at West Point, the President restored Partridge to duty and gave him the chance to resign from the army, which he did.[41]

Following his career at West Point, Partridge became military instructor to a volunteer corps, which was to be the beginning of his continued interest in the organization and training of volunteer militia. In addition to his work in establishing various schools, he engaged in the survey of the Northeastern Boundary of the United States, was surveyor general of Vermont and served as representative from his town of Norwich to the state legislature. Dartmouth College conferred the degree of M.A. in course upon Partridge in 1812, and in 1821 the University of Vermont conferred upon him the honorary degree of A.M. In this year 1821 the University of Vermont had elected him president, a position he was unable to accept.[42]

The Academy at Norwich.—Partridge's experience at West Point convinced him that the National Academy would not be able to satisfy the needs of officers for the army and militia nor would it train the number of engineers necessary for the development of the country. For this reason he conceived the plan of a civilian institution for the training of soldiers and engineers. When he presented this plan to the public he received offers of money and land from a number of towns with the provision that the school would be located within their borders. He settled on his native town of Norwich, Vermont, whose citizens provided a site for the Academy and money to build a barrack. This new institution he named the American Literary, Scientific and Military Academy. Within the year a brick building four stories high, 100 feet long, and 50 feet wide was constructed; the new school enrolled 100 students on September 4, 1820. These students came from eleven states and one foreign country. The catalogue published in 1821 gives the attendance as 117, distributed as follows: Vermont 54, New Hempshire 26, Massachusetts 11, New York 7, Maine 4, South Carolina 4, Connecticut 3, Michigan Territory 2, Georgia 2, Ohio 1, Louisiana 1, Pennsylvania 1, and Canada 1.[43]

With respect to enrollment, it is of interest that it was 135 in 1822, 158 in 1823, and 162 in 1824. The faculty for 1821 consisted of seven members and increased to thirteen professors and eleven instructors by 1826, when the enrollment was 293. The relative size of this young school is better understood by comparing it with Dartmouth, which had 150 students in 1810.

[40] Sidney Forman, *op. cit.,* p. 40.
[41] *Ibid.,* p. 44.
[42] G. M. Dodge, W. A. Ellis, *op. cit.,* (Vol. 2) p. 25.
[43] *Ibid.,* (Vol. 1) p. 5.

The Academy was patterned after West Point, with the exception that no specified time was required for completing the course. Partridge maintained that one of the weaknesses of the traditional institution was having the good student held back by what he termed the "sluggard." No regular graduations were held, as the student received a certificate when he completed the course. A study of the biographical sketches of the first graduates indicates that cadets attended the Academy for a period of from two to three years. The course of study is best described by the first catalogue:

> The course of education at this seminary will embrace the following branches of literature, science and practical instruction, viz: the Latin, Greek, Hebrew, French and the English Languages: Composition, Rhetoric, Logic, Elocution: History, Geography, including the use of maps and globes: Ethics, Metaphysics: the elements of Natural and Political Law, the Law of Nations, the Constitution of the United States and of the States severally, Military Law: the elements of Chemistry, Electricity and Optics: Arithmetic, the construction and use of Logarithms, Bookkeeping, Algebra, Geometry, Plane and Spherical Trigonometry, Planometry, Sterometry, Mensuration of heights and distances by Trigonometry and also Geometrically, practical Geometry generally, including particularly, Surveying and Levelling, Conic Sections, the use of the Barometer, wth its application to measuring the altitudes of mountains and other eminences: Mechanics, Hydrostatics, Hydraulics, Astronomy, Navigation, Civil Engineering, including the construction of roads, canals, locks, and bridges: Architecture, Agriculture, Music.[44]

The Academy at Middletown, Connecticut.—In 1824 Partridge determined to move the Academy from Norwich to Connecticut. No reason has been advanced as to why he made this change. The school relocated in Middletown where the town's people provided the land and built some buildings. In this location the Academy continued to prosper with its enrollment approximating 300 students. The Academy did not obtain the support of the Connecticut legislature desired by Partridge. In this regard the state denied the school power to confer degrees, but permitted a lottery to raise $40,000 for the purchase of chemical, astronomical and philosophical apparatus, and for a library and buildings. Partridge felt that he was not receiving sufficient support and determined to make no further efforts on behalf of the institution in Middletown. The net result was that in 1829 the buildings became the property of Wesleyan University and the Academy as such was discontinued in Connecticut.

Norwich University.—In 1829 the Academy was reopened at Norwich, but from 1829 to 1834 little is known of its activities. In November, 1834, the legislature granted a charter changing the American Literary, Scientific and Military Academy to Norwich University. The instruction at the University was divided into four departments: Collegiate, Civil Engineering, Teach-

[44] *Ibid.,* p. 13.

ers, and Primary. The last department was dropped in 1838. The course of study in engineering is described as follows:

> The instruction in the department of Engineering embraced the following subjects: Algebra, Geometry, construction and use of Logarithms, Plane and Spherical Trigonometry, Mensuration of Heights and Distances, Planometry, Stereometry, Practical Geometry generally, including particularly Surveying and Levelling, Descriptive Geometry, Conic Sections, Mechanics, Statics, Hydrostatics, Chemistry, Geology, Architecture, Construction of Common Roads and Railroads, Canals, Locks, Bridges, Aqueducts, Viaducts; also the English and French Languages, Geography and History. Much practical field work was given. The students in this department were carefully trained in Declamation, weekly exercises in composition being required.[45]

A study of the alumni biographies shows that the first engineering degrees were awarded in 1837, when two students recived the M.C.E. degree after completing a three year course of study. The alumni of those institutions that had been sponsored by Partridge entered both the military and civil life. Norwich has always maintained a department of civil engineering, but the numbers it has graduated have been small. It did, however, provide evidence of the public's willingness to accept a new type of education that was not to become common until fifty years after the American Literary, Scientific and Military Academy was founded by Partridge in 1819.

The Gardiner Lyceum

Robert H. Gardiner and Benjamin Hale.—The founding and operation of the Gardiner Lyceum was mainly the work of Robert H. Gardiner, who established the institution, and Benjamin Hale who operated it.

Robert Gardiner was born in Bristol, England, in 1782 and came to the United States with his parents in 1792, when they returned to America after leaving as royalists in 1776. At the age of five he inherited a considerable fortune from his maternal grandfather and assumed the surname of Gardiner to comply with his grandfather's will. His father's name was Hallowell. Gardiner was educated at Boston Latin School, Phillips Andover Academy, and graduated from Harvard College in 1801. He revisited Europe to study agricultural and manufacturing methods and later operated an experimental farm at Gardiner, Maine. He was a member of the Maine Legislature in 1822, overseer and trustee of Bowdoin College and President of the Maine Historical Society from 1845 to 1855.[46]

Benjamin Hale was born in Newburyport, Massachusetts, in 1797 and graduated from Bowdoin College in 1818. After teaching in the Saco Academy for one year and studying Theology during another year, he returned

---

[45] *Ibid.*, p. 75-76.
[46] "Robert H. Gardiner," *Dictionary of American Biography* (Vol. 7, 1936) p. 137.

to Bowdoin College as a teacher of science. In 1823 he became principal of the Gardiner Lyceum, where he remained until 1827. In that year he accepted a professorship of chemistry at Dartmouth which he held until 1835. His preaching in Episcopal Churches offended Congregational feeling at Dartmouth, with the result that the professorship of chemistry was secretly abolished, Hale being notified after the college President and trustees had left Hanover. In 1835 he was made President of Hobert College, which was then Geneva College, a position he successfully administered until ill health caused his resignation in 1858.[47]

The Gardiner Lyceum.—The educational motives of Gardiner in incorporating a Lyceum in 1822 were not the same as those of Partridge three years earlier when he established his Academy. Partridge believed that the type of educational program developed at West Point should be made available to those who deserved it, and should not be restricted to government appointees alone. Gardiner and Hale were interested in developing a distinctly new type of collegiate institution that had gradually been evolving over a period of years. It differed from the mechanics institutes and the Lyceums then starting by requiring the full time of students and providing a curriculum preparatory to the higher studies of agriculture, mechanics, arts and engineering. The regular curriculum of the Lyceum was not too different from that of Partridge's Academy, but its special courses and objectives varied considerably. In fact, in many features of its operation it anticipated the Morrill Act of 1862. Specifically these features were: state financial support, teaching short courses for those not taking full courses, the introduction of practicalships for student instructors and the operation of an experimental farm by the students.

The original objective is best stated in a report of the Committee on Literary Institutions of the Maine State Senate as follows:

> Its object was to give the laboring class of the community such a scientific education, as was principally adapted to their wants, and to give such an education as could not be obtained at other Schools and Academies in order to enable our young men, designed for active business, to obtain a practical, scientific education, without subjecting them to the expense and loss of time required, to go through a collegiate course.[48]

In an address to the public Gardiner expressed the confidence that the state would assist in the support of the Lyceum. In this same report, he stated that a student would complete in two years what is an essential course, but that instruction would be provided for those desiring a third year. The public

[47] "Benjamin Hale," *Dictionary of American Biography* (Vol. 8, 1936) p. 96.
[48] Report of the Committee on Literary Institutions, on the Petition of the Trustees of Gardiner Lyceum, February 25, 1832 (Printed by Order of the Senate of the State of Maine.)

was also informed that Rev. Benjamin Hale, recently a tutor in Bowdoin College, was elected Principal of the Lyceum, and lecturer in Natural Philosophy.[49]

Benjamin Hale in his inaugural address restated the views of Gardiner that "There surely can be no reason why mechanics and agriculturists should not be instructed in that science, which will enable them to follow their pursuits, not blindly, but from rational views."[50]

For its establishment, $1,650 was subscribed for the erection of a building together with a donation of 312 acres of land. Classes were started in January, 1823, with twenty students enrolled, ten being in the third or youngest class, and ten in the second class. The studies of the first year were the same for all and consisted chiefly of elementary mathematics. The catalogue stated that the mathematics taught was selected and translated from the works of the most eminent French mathematicians, for the use of the students at the University of Cambridge. The course of study, including the short courses as well as the regular curriculum is given in the 1827 catalogue as follows:

First year. Arithmetic, Geography, Bookkeeping, Algebra, Geometry, Mensuration, and Linear Drawing.
Second year. Trigonometry, Surveying, Navigation, application of Algebra and Geometry, Differential and Integral Calculus, Mechanics, Perspective, Chemistry and Agricultural Chemistry. Instead of the last mentioned study, Civil Engineering is pursued by those who prefer it.
Third year. Natural Philosophy, Astronomy, Political Economy, the Federalist, History, Mineralogy, Natural History, Natural Theology.

Besides the above, Blair's Rhetoric is studied during the first and second years, and the Evidences of Christianity during the second and third years. The students in the two higher classes are also instructed in composition and declamation.

In addition to the three regular classes, extra classes are admitted to pursue particular courses of study, viz: one in Civil Architecture, admitted in November, and instructed in Geometry, Architectural Drawing, the mechanical principles of Carpentry, etc.; a second in Surveying, admitted in September; a third in Navigation, admitted in September and May; a fourth in Chemistry, admitted in January; and a fifth in Agriculture admitted in November, and instructed in Agricultural Chemistry, Anatomy and diseases of domestic animals, and such parts of Natural History as are peculiarly interesting to the agriculturist. The first and fifth of the above classes continued for about four months, the others, three. (4-11, 216)[51]

[49] Benjamin Hale, An Inaugural Address (Gardiner, Maine: S. K. Gilman Printer, 1823) p. 15 (Original copy in Bowdoin College Library)

[50] R. H. Gardiner, An Address to the Public from the Trustees of the Gardiner Lyceum, Printed by Goodale Galzier and Company, 1822, (Original copy in Bowdoin College Library, New Brunswick, Maine, and a copy in Crosby Library, Gonzaga University, Spokane, Washington.)

[51] C. A. Bennet, History of Manual and Industrial Education Up to 1870 (Peoria, Illinois: C. A. Bennet Company, 1926) p. 349.

The experimental farm is best described in the catalogue of 1833:

> The principal objects which the trustees have in view, in establishing the professorship in connection with a practical farm: 1st, to give the future agriculturist the knowledge of those principles of science upon which his future success depends, and to let him see them reduced to practice. 2nd, To furnish a beneficial employment as recreation. 3rd, To diminish the expenses of board, and 4th. to try a series of agricultural experiments adapted to the soil and climate of Maine. These experiments will be tried by the students, under the direction of the professor, and will be conducted with as much care and accuracy, as the nature of the case will admit.[52]

To support the school the State legislature in 1823 granted $2,000 and some land. For a number of years following this the state granted the school $1,000 per year. The first year Hale was the only teacher, but in the fall of 1823 two additional instructors were employed. For its ten years of existence the student body varied from twenty students to sixty-six students. Hale resigned in 1827 when it had reached its zenith. Neither Hale nor Gardiner was the promoter that Partridge was and the school was closed in 1832 when the state legislature withdrew its support. The institution was an important element in the development of technical education in general, and engineering education in particular, because of the innovations it introduced. The new elements of state support, a curriculum with uniform freshmen year, an experimental farm, and development of courses to meet local need justifies its consideration rather than the number of graduates supplied.

The Rensselaer School

Buel's Proposal Without State Aid.—Buel's proposal that the New York State Legislature establish a tax supported school of agriculture contained the condition that, for such an institution, Stephan Rensselaer would donate the necessary land. As previously stated, the legislature in 1823 failed to create the desired school. Van Rensselaer, to assure himself that such a school would be successful, employed Professor Eaton to give a series of demonstrated lectures on chemistry, natural philosophy, and natural history in the principal towns of northern New York State. Encouraged by the success of this undertaking he determined to establish a school whose principal object would be:

> . . . to qualify teachers for instructing the sons and daughters of farmers and mechanics, by lectures or otherwise, in the application of experimental chemistry, philosophy, and natural history to agriculture, domestic economy, the arts, and manufactures.[53]

[52] 1923 Catalogue, *op. cit., p.*
[53] P. C. Ricketts, *op. cit.,* p. 18.

Thus was the Rensselaer School established in 1824 in Troy, New York. Van Rensselaer specified many of the details concerning the school's management, and in stating its purpose used the expression of Count Rumford: "To give instruction in the application of science to the common purposes of life." The purpose of providing teachers of agriculture is understandable, considering that Van Rensselaer owned a tract of land now consisting of three counties in eastern New York State. This land he leased out, and it was to his advantage to have his tenants practice improved methods of agriculture.

Stephan Van Rensselaer and Amos Eaton.—Van Rensselaer was born in New York City in 1764. He graduated from Harvard College in 1782 and while in college was a member of the scientific group organized by Samuel Williams in the Scientific expedition of 1780. During his life he busied himself with public affairs and with the management of his inherited property. His activity in public life consisted of being state senator, lieutenant governor, regent of Union College, member of the constitutional convention and a United States Congressman from the state of New York.

In this last position it was he who cast the deciding vote electing John Quincy Adams as President of the United States over Andrew Jackson and William Crawford in the election of 1824. After promising not to vote for Adams, he was somewhat confused, and went to his seat and sent up a prayer to determine his vote's direction. Glancing at the floor, he saw an old ballot market "John Q. Adams" which he took as being a sign from heaven and caused him to stuff it into the ballot box, thus electing John Quincy Adams President of the United States.[54]

Amos Eaton (1776-1842) was born in Chatham, New York, and graduated from Williams College in 1799. Upon graduation he prepared for and practiced law until 1815, when he gave it up to study chemistry, geology, and mineralogy under Professor Stillman at Yale. In 1819 Eaton returned to Williams College as Professor of Science and became famous for his teaching, publications, and explorations. Although he was nationally known for his geological work, his greatest fame rests on his work as senior professor at Rensselaer, where he taught for seventeen years and was responsible for the educational program adopted by that institution. Baker states that:

> Amos Eaton was an original genius of profound and far reaching intellect. Local tradition well authenticated, credits him with the inception of the institute; and certainly Van Rensselaer's letter announcing the organization of the school bears evidence of his hand. In fact, until 1840 his influence was supreme.[55]

[54] John F. Fitzpatrick (ed) *Autobiography of Martin Van Buren* (Annual Report of the American Historical Society, Vol. 2) p. 149.

[55] R. P. Palmer, A *Chapter in American Education* (New York: Charles Scribner's Sons, 1924) p. 10.

The Rensselaer School.—The school was established in 1824 and the word "Engineer" or engineering did not appear in the bill of incorporation or in any part of the first pamphlet of forty-six pages.[56] The school started to do essentially what its founder proposed in a notice signed by the President, Dr. Blatchford, printed in the Troy Sentinel of December 28, 1824.

> The Hon. Stephen Van Rensselaer having established a school near the northern limits of Troy for teaching the physical sciences with their application to the arts of life; having appointed Profs. A. Eaton and L. C. Beck to give courses of instruction particularly calculated to prepare operative chemists and practical naturalists properly qualified to act as teachers in villages and school districts; having appointed an agent and furnished him with funds for procuring apparatus and fitting up a laboratory, library room, etc.; and the agent having given notice to the president of the institution that the requisite collections and preparations are completed, it seems proper to give public notice of these circumstances.
>
> Accordingly the public is respectfully notified that everything is in readiness at the Rensselaer School for giving instruction in chemistry, experimental philosophy and natural history, with their application to agriculture, domestic economy, and the arts; and also for teaching land surveying . . .
>
> During the day no lectures will be given by the professors, but under their superintendence the students, divided into sections, will perform all the experiments and give the explanations, the students thus acting as lecturers and the professors as auditors . . .
>
> Students who wish for extra accomodations will pay from $1.75 to $2.00 per week for board and lodging. But any number of students can have good plain board and lodging near the school for $1.50 per week.[57]

The above letter describes the type of institution that characterized the school for many years. In fact the individual effort of the students regulated the number of teachers by assigning one teacher to each section of five or six students. This made the cost of operation excessive; and in 1827 the president, at the suggestion of the founder, offered the school to the legislature as an institution to train teachers. This was in line with the founder's original intention of supporting the school for three years, with the thought that once it proved its worth the public would support it. This did not turn out to be the case, and as the support of the school was becoming burdensome to Van Rensselaer, he signified to the trustees his desire to discontinue it in 1829. In November, 1829, Eaton was constituted the "agent" of the trustees, and as such was authorized to receive and expend all moneys at his discretion and to retain all profits for his own benefit.[58] The arrangement continued for one

[56] A. M. Wellington, "Rensselaer Polytechnic Institute," *The Engineering News*, Vol. 27 (April 12, 1892) p. 313.
[57] Palmer C. Ricketts, *History of Rensselaer Polytechic Institute 1824-1934* (New York: John Wiley and Sons, Inc., 1934) p. 31-32.
[58] P. C. Ricketts, *op. cit.*, p. 64.

year only, but the school continued to exist after 1830 by contributions from its founder and by improvements made in instructional methods. In all Rensselaer contributed $22,000 to the founding and support of the school.

The Operation of Rensselaer School.—From the time of its establishment in 1824 to 1834 the number of students at any one time never exceeded and was generally less than 25. The course was of one year's duration, and up to the year 1834 the degree of bachelor of arts, A.B. (rs) was the only one conferred. In 1835 the degree of bachelor of natural science (BNS) replaced the arts degree, and in addition the CE degree was introduced for a one year course. The degree of Master of Arts was conferred on graduates after two years of practical application. Many of the students were well prepared upon entrance, as the average age was twenty and Eaton stated that the course was intended for those who had completed their academic education. To this end a separated preparatory branch was established in 1826 to accommodate those who were disqualified for the entrance to the Rensselaer school by want of education or because they were under seventeen years of age. In 1830, when the school's purpose was changing, Eaton considered it a common workshop for all colleges, academies and other literary and scientific seminaries of learning.[59] At one time twelve of the twenty-five students were graduates of other colleges. This concept of being a graduate school anticipated Gilman's John Hopkins University by half of a century.

The purpose of the early curriculum was to prepare teachers for scientific and practical subjects. To further satisfy this end a scholarship was offered to one student from each county in 1827. Each student so selected was required to teach the experimental and demonstrative method in his own county for a period of one year. Educational method was not taught as a course but was incorporated in all subjects by having students lecture on each subject assigned. The curriculum of 1825 is embodied in the first three articles of the by-laws:

> Article I. The course of exercises at said school in the Fall Term shall be as nearly as circumstances will permit, as follows: Each student shall give five lectures each week on systematic botany, demonstrated with specimens, for the first three weeks, and shall either collect, analyze and preserve specimens of plants, or examine the operations of artists and manufacturers at the school workshops, under the direction of a professor or assistant, who shall explain the scientific principles upon which such operations, depend, four hours on each of the six days in every week, unless excused by a professor on account of the weather. Each student shall give fifteen lectures on metalloids, metals, soils, manures, mineral waters, and animal and vegetable matter— all to be fully illustrated with experiments performed with his own hands; and shall examine the operations of artists at the school workshops, under the direc-

59 R. P. Baker, *op. cit.,* p. 23.

tion of a professor or assistant, four hours on every Saturday, unless excused as aforesaid.

Article 2. During the Winter Term students shall recite, to a professor or to a competent assistant, the elements of the sciences taught in the fall and spring terms; and shall study and recite, as auxiliary branches in aid of these sciences, rhetoric, logic, geography, as much mathematics as the faculty shall deem necesary for studying land surveying, common mensuration, and for performing the common astronomical calculations.

Article 3. The course of exercises in the Spring Term shall be, as nearly as circumstances will admit, as follows: Each student shall, during the first six weeks, give ten lectures on experimental philosophy; ten lectures on metalloids, metals, soils and mineral waters; ten lectures on chemical powers and on substances not metallic. For the remainder of the term each student shall be exercised in the application of the sciences before enumerated to the analysis of particular selected specimens of soils, manures, animal and vegetable substances, ores, and mineralwaters; and shall devote four hours of each day, unless excused by one of the faculty, to the examination of the operations of the agriculturist on the school farms, together with progress of cultivated grains, grasses, fruit-trees, and other plants, to practical land-surveying and general mensuration, to calculations upon the application of water-power and steam which is made to the various machines in the vicinity of the school, and to an examination of the laws of hydrostatics and hydrodynamics which are exemplified by the locks, and canals, aqueducts, and natural waterfalls surrounding the institution.[60]

The first mention of civil engineering appeared in the catalogue of 1828 when the senior instructor was listed as giving lectures in land surveying and civil engineering. While there was no specific curriculum in civil engineering, the courses added each year tended to strengthen this subject. It was not until 1835 that a special department of Mathematical Arts was established to offer a degree and specific instruction in engineering and technology.

The foregoing is presented to show that Rensselaer was not started as a school of engineering. It was ten years before it gave full acceptance to the idea of this type of training. The initial history of the school or the institute as it became in 1833, is of value in showing how under Eaton's direction the institution's purpose was changed to meet new conditions. By adjustments of its program its chief work rapidly passed into the realm in which it became famous. This transformation into an institution comparable to what the French had developed was far from complete in this period. For the complete change to take place required the foresight and effort of Benjamin Green, who became director in 1847.

[60] C. P. Ricketts, op. cit., p. 38-39.

chapter 4

The Definitive Stage in American Engineering Education (1835-1863)

Development of the Period

Introduction.—Between the year 1835 to 1863 many significant changes occurred in America that effected the progress of engineering education. At the beginning of the period the panic of 1837 discouraged the starting of new institutions. Over the period, however, basic changes toward industrialization were continuous, as the precentage of the urban population increased from 8.9 percent to 19.7 percent while the total population increased from approximately 12,000,000 in 1830 to 31,000,000 in 1860.[1] This rapid change in the size and distribution of population, caused by native births and a wave of imigrants from Europe, was accompanied by significant transportation, industrial, social, and cultural changes. These forces changed the character of Rensselaer Institute and caused a few schools to be founded. The new institutions were of different types, and set the patterns for the many new technical schools that were to be created in the period immediately following the civil war. Although the forces at work in this period defined the type, organization, and need for engineering education, there were still lacking ways by which to establish the schools so defined. To understand these influences that created a need, without offering an accompanying solution, an analysis of some of the many-sided developments of the times is in order.

Construction and Industry.—Canal building which had reached its peak by 1840 was replaced by an expansion in the construction of surfaced roads constructed and by the rapidly expanding railroad movement. The mileage of public roads increased from 47,562 in 1835 to 91,094 in 1865.[2] During the same period the mileage of railroads increased from 1,098 to 35,085.[3] These railroads required large investments since the cost of track building ranged from ten to sixty thousand dollars per mile. This financial demand was

[1] Bureau of Census, *Historical Statistics of the United States* 1789-1945 (Washington, D. C.: United States Department of Commerce) p. 26.
[2] *Ibid.*, p. 220.
[3] *Ibid.*, p. 300.

53

more than private subscription could meet, with the result that a dozen states made surveys, loaned money, purchased stock and even did outright building.[4]

Manufacturing extended beyond the already established textile mills and iron works, and the chief agricultural produce changed from tobacco to cotton. At this time America was not behind Europe in inventions; the number of patents increased from 200 in 1820 to 30,000 in 1870. In this regard states:

> The very volume of important inventions overwhelms any investigator. Agricultural machines ran from well-drilling machinery and the reaper to a sausage-filling machine and a lactometer. The homes received new stoves, refrigerators, and dishwashing machines. The Colt revolver was revolutionary—a bad pun. The suspension bridge was made practical by John Roebling's wire rope. Diving suits were expected to replace the diving bell, and a submarine telescope was invented, while Fulton's submarine was available. Various flying machines were patented—usually a balloon with wings like a bird's. An Illinois pioneer tried to fly a monoplane with wings which were flapped by a crank; he failed.[5]

Of the eleven great inventions of these years of the industrial revolution, Chase notes that all but three were American contributions. The portion of his complete list that applies to the time being considered is given in Table 1.

TABLE I

SOME OF THE GREAT INVENTIONS OF THE INDUSTRIAL REVOLUTION*

Date	Invention	Inventor	Country
1835	Electric telegraph	Morse	U. S.
1835	Revolver	Colt	U. S.
1837	Electric motor	Davenport	U. S.
1839	Electrotype	Daguerre	France
1840	Steamhammer	Nasmyth	England
1845	Turret Lathe	Filch (Stephen)	U. S.
1846	Sewing Machine	Howe	U. S.
1847	Rotary Press	Hoe	U. S.
1851	Electric Locomotive	Vail	U. S.
1861	Machine Gun	Gatling	U. S.
1865	Bessemer Steel	Bessemer	England
1865	Bessemer Steel	Kelley	U. S.

*Stuart Chase, *Men and Machines* (New York: McMillan Co., 1928) p.78-79

Education and Culture.—As machinery and processes became more common, as state geological surveys revealed our mineral potential, and as needs on all sides pressed for the full development of our national economy, many new kinds of training became necessary. As civil engineering had developed to meet the needs not satisfied by the military engineer, so in this

[4] Robert E. Riegel, *Young America 1830-1840* (Norman, Oklahoma: University of Oklahoma Press, 1941) p. 173.
[5] *Ibid.,* p. 327.

period mechanical engineering and mining engineering were developed to meet requirements not satisfied by civil engineering. The course in mechanical engineering was new. While mining engineering was new to this country, it was well developed in Europe where the Bergakademie in Germany dated back to 1765 and the Ecole des Mines in France to 1778. Large private sums were not available for the founding of many of these new schools. In Massachusetts, for example, from the year 1859 to 1861, of the 15,285 estates of men dying only seven had an average value of $848,700.[6] The obtaining of small sums from a large number of people would have proved difficult, as the money value of goods possessed by the American people in 1860 was only $513.93 per capita.[7]

The small number of engineering schools started between 1835 and 1863 was not indicative of a lack of interest in technical education or in the development of a national culture. The facts are to the contrary. Many plans and petitions were made to state legislatures requesting the establishment and support of technical schools. The newly created laboring class supported the movement for free public education that was gradually replacing tthe tuition academy. Mechanics Institutes, an institution developed in England, were found in practically all the large industrial centers. Their purposes, not unlike those ascribed to our present day junior colleges, were well stated at the opening of the Boston Mechanics Institute by George Emerson:

> To give to persons, whose time is chiefly occupied with business or labor, knowledge of a kind to be directly useful to them in their daily pursuits . . . The principles of science have hitherto been accessible to those only who are pursuing a course of study preparatory to what are called the liberal professions. The poor and the occupied, if destined to the active pursuits of life, have been almost necessarily debarred from them. By Mechanics Institutions they are offered to all, to the busy, the poor and the uninformed.[8]

Following the Mechanics Institute and in some cases with it was the mechanics library, which is well described by Shera:

> Concern with the problems confronting the workers did not leave the library untouched. To some extent labor leadership participated in the movement for library establishments, as it had showed in support of public schools. In the case of the library, the vocational interests of the workers made its greatest contributions in the form of mechanic's and mercantile libraries that appeared during the first half of the nineteenth century and in the factory book collection in a few industrial towns.[9]

6 William I. King, *The Wealth and Income of the People of the United States* (New York: Macmillan Company, 1923) p. 68.

7 *Ibid.*, p. 13.

8 George G. Emerson, "Mechanics Institutions," *American Journal of Education*, 1827, p. 68.

9 Jesse H. Shera, *Foundation of the Public Library* (Chicago, Illinois: University of Chicago Press, 1949) p. 230.

To illustrate the popularity of the movement, Brooks tells of Agassiz being present at an assembly of three thousand mechanics brought together to form a library. These same men listened for two hours with rapt attention to a lecture on the advantages of reading.[10] This material is presented to show that while public education was just getting a good start the needs of the working people were recognized. More than this, however, was the attitude of the workers themselves. The intense desire for knowledge on their part found expression in the Lyceum movement, which appealed to both men and women.

The American Lyceum was founded by Joseph Holbrook in 1826 and by the beginning of this period 3,000 lyceums had been established in towns and cities throughout the United States, providing the most important stimulus to general education up to that time.[11] The effectiveness of this program and the degree of public interest in it are vividly described by Brooks, speaking of the girls in the Lowell textile mills.

> Dickens was impressed by the interests of the factory girls of Lowell, a public that he knew so well in England. There were joint-stock pianos in their boarding-houses; the walls of the mills were covered with their poems; they subscribed to the British Reviews; they had classes in German; they all seemed to know "Paradise Lost" by heart and talked about Wordsworth, Coleridge, and Macauley in the intervals of changing bobbins on the looms. Flocks of these serious girls, described by Lucy Larcom in her *Idle of Works* afterward went West as school teachers and founded "Improvement Circles" on the prairies. The fame of the Lowell Offering, which contained their writings—humorous and pathetic tales, fairy stories, poems,—traveled around the World. A volume of selections, "Mind Among the Spindles," was later published in London, and lectures were given at the Sorbonne on this portent of the times.[12]

Concurrent with the Mechanics Institutes, the Mechanics and Mercantile Libraries, the Lyceum movement, and the beginnings of our public school system was the development of an American literature that had its origins in New England. Not inconsistent with this pattern was the large number of American intellectuals studying in Europe. They were there to obtain specialized training not available at home and to determine what European educational practices could be transplanted to the benefit of America's national growth. Those engaged in foreign study and travel were not limited to such classical scholars as Tichnor, Bancroft, and Everett, but included such people as Greene, Rogers and Egleston. Greene improved the curriculum of Rens-

---

[10] Van Wyck Brooks, *The Flowering of New England* (New York: E. P. Dutton and Company, 1940) p. 176.
[11] James D. Hart, *Oxford Companion to American Literature* (New York: Oxford University Press, 1941) p. 492.
[12] Van Wyck Brooks, *op. cit.*, p. 177.

selaer Institute, Rogers founded Massachusetts Institute of Technology and Egleston helped organize the Columbia School of Mines.

Such intellectual activities were not restricted to the above mentioned cases. In higher education there was an amazing multiplication of small denominational colleges. Morison described the situation as follows:

> In 16 Eastern and Mid-Western states (both North and South) no less than 516 colleges and universities were founded before the Civil War; but only 104 of these were still in existence in 1929. Yale alone begot 16 Congregationist colleges before 1861, and Princeton, 25 Presbyterian ones. These institutions were all privately endowed, in some instances by funds contributed directly by the churches. It was the heyday of the small, rural college with six to a dozen professors and one to three hundred students; of six o'clock chapel, prescribed classical-mathematical course, with chemistry and physics the most popular subjects next to Greek, and a smattering of French and German; philosophical apparatus, mineralogical cabinet etc.[13]

The above number of 516 colleges at the time of the Civil War contrasts sharply with the 99 existing in 1830. The gowth of the traditional liberal arts colleges was not the only form of higher education that experienced an abnormal gain. The professional schools of theology, medicine and law also shared in this rapid growth. In 1850 there were 72 theological, 48 medical, 18 law and 3 dental schools in America.[14] For the most part these institutions were independently operated and not connected with any existing college or university. With the exception of the Theological schools, they were profit-making schools and not endowed by private funds or supported by the state. They were organized by members of their respective professions, with a curriculum determined by the profession to meet its specific need. As such they included few if any general education courses, and established a pattern that in many respects persists to this day.

This extended treatment of the intellectual development of the period has been presented to indicate that technical education, of a professional nature, could well have shared in the general movement had ways been devised to support it financially. The need and the interest, as attested to by the many petitions to the state legislatures, was present. The states had not as yet fully developed their public secondary schools and were not receptive to the new idea of supporting higher technical schools, nor were large sums from private sources readily available. The large number of schools for professions other than engineering were operated only because they were private ventures, an organizational form never adopted by engineering education. The accomplishments of the period were therefore restricted to the founding of a few schools

13 S. E. Morison and H. S. Commager, *The Growth of the American Republic* (New York: Oxford University Press, 1937) Vol. 1, p. 409.
14 N. M. Butler, *Professional Education in the United States* (New York: American Book Company, 1910) p. 466.

that established the type of schools to be later multiplied in numbers. It is to a discussion of these developments that the remainder of the chapter will be devoted.

Reorganization of Rensselaer

Civil Engineering Introduced. — As previously stated, from 1824 to 1835 Rensselaer Institute operated as a combination teacher-training and general science school. Civil Engineering was first mentioned in the 1828 catalogue. In 1835 a one-year course in Civil Engineering was authorized, and in that year four candidates for the degree recommended in the following letter from examiners dated Oct. 14, 1835:

> We have examined Edward Suffern, William Clement, Jacob Eddy, and Amos Westcott as candidates for the degree of Civil Engineer. We find them acquainted with the theory of practice. But as this is the first class proposed to graduate, their own honor and the honor of this institution demand great caution in conferring degrees. We therefore, recommend as follows: that they receive the degrees but that the diplomas be left with the Secretary until the President shall receive satisfactcory certificates that they have reviewed their text books, that they can read algebraic equations, and have a general knowledge of Perspective generally.[15]

> A. R. Judah, *Chairman*
> P. H. Green,
> Harvey Warner,—*Examiners*

For the next thirteen years, up to the year 1848, this one-year course was all that Rensselaer offered in engineering. During this period the school was small, with an attendance of 77 in 1839 and 22 in 1848. Approximately 85% of the students were residents of the state of New York.

In 1842 Amos Eaton died and, after a number of short term professors held office, B. Franklin Greene was appointed in 1846. Greene had graduated from Rensselaer in 1842 with the degrees of civil engineer and bachelor of natural sciences and had been teaching at Washington College since 1843. In 1849 he was responsible for the complete reorganization of Rensselaer, which included a new definition of its purpose and a curriculum to carry out the new aims and objectives. The new plan is best described by quoting the following part of the eighty-seven page pamphlet published in 1855 and entitled "The Rensselaer Polytechnic Institute: Its Reorganization In 1849-50; Its Condition at the Present Time; Its Plans and Hopes for the Future."

> The managers of the Institute therefore resolved that their field should be narrowed and more thoroughly cultivated; that, indeed, their educational objects should be restricted to matters immediately cognate to Architecture and Engineering; that, moreover, for a somewhat irregular

---

[15] Palmer C. Ricketts, *History of Rensselaer Polytechnic Institute* VRBD-VTCD (New York: John Wiley & Sons, Inc., 1934) p. 81-82.

and for the most part optional course, requiring but a single year for its accomplishment, they would substitute a carefully considered curriculum which should require at the least three full years of systematic and thorough training; and that, finally, they would demand the application of the strictest examination tests to the successive parts of the course prescribed, not only in respect to the translation of students from lower classes, but, especially, in all cases of ultimate graduation with professional degrees. It was in accordance with such views as these that, in 1849-50, this institution was wholly reorganized upon the basis of a general polytechnic institute, when it received the distinctive addition to its title, under which it has since been more or less generally known. Its objects were thenceforward declared to be the "education of architects and civil, mining, and topographical engineers, upon an enlarged basis and with a liberal development of mental and physical culture."

But it is proper to remark that, with the comprehensive statement and formal announcement then made, of what was proposed to be the future work of the Institute, there was associated in the minds of its managers no immediate expectations of realizing more than a very partial development of their plans, with the comparatively limited resources in materials of every kind at their command. Accordingly it was resolved that, of the entire Institute curriculum, they would at first proceed to develop the General Course—the common scientific basis of the four professional courses—and the two specialities of Civil and Topographical Engineering, to as good a degree of excellence as should be practicable under the existing circumstances; while they would defer any attempt to effect the more complete development of their plans, including the important specialities of Architecture and Mining Engineering to a period when they might hope to be able to invoke effectively the aid of conditions more favorable to realizations so desirable.[16]

The above statement established a broad base for the curriculum and was a declaration of intention with respect to offering fields of engineering other than civil. In this regard topographical engineering was offered as a degree program from 1850 to 1866, when it was replaced by mining engineering. Mechanical engineering was added in 1862. The course of Architecture referred to in the reorganization was not offered because of lack of funds. Although Greene had a curriculum designed for Architecture it was not until 1929 that one was in operation at Rensselaer.

Prior to initiating his reorganization plans Greene made a careful study of technical institutions in Europe. This study not only had a profound effect on the curriculum of Rensselaer, but also served to define the engineering curriculum in America. The basic curriculum adopted was very similar to that of the Ecole Centrale of Paris. Once adopted by Rensselaer it served as the model for other schools. The following table will show how this curriculum compares with those of the Ecole Centrale, the Massachusetts Institute of Technology and the University of Illinois.

16 *Ibid.*, p. 93-94.

TABLE 2
AIMS AND CURRICULA OF THE EARLY SCHOOLS

Ecole Centrale 1850	Rensselaer 1849-1850	M.I.T. 1865	Univ. of Illinois 1867
First Year			
Descrip. Geo.	Alg., Geo., Trig.	Alg., Sol. Geo.,	Calcu., Geo.
Math. Anal. Mech.	Gen. Physics	Trig.	Trig.,
Kinematics	Geo. Drawing	El. Mech	Descrip. Geo.
Gen. Chem.	English	Drawing	Eng. or Foreign
Hygiene &	Foreign Lang.	English	Language
Nat. Hist.	Surveying	Foreign Lang.	History
Drawing	Botany	Inorg. Chem.	Botany
Second Year			
Descrip. Geo.	Anal. Calcu.	Anal. Calcu.	Anal. Calcu.
Mechanics	Gen. Phy.	Physics	Descrip. Geo.
Mat. of Constr.	Chem.	Chemistry	Surveying
Industr. Phy	Des. Geo.	Descrip. Geo.	Foreign Lang.
Anal. Chem	Mech. Draw.	Mach. &	
Chem. of Indust.	Topograph., &	Freehand	
Minerals	Hydrograph.	Surv.—plane	
Geology	Surv.	English	
Pub. Works	English	Foreign Lang.	
Mfg. (Iron & Steel)	Foreign Lang.	Astron., Nav.	
Tech. (Cordage,	Mineralogy		
tex., mat., cutting,	Zoology		
of wood &	Geology		
stone, etc.)			
Third Year			
Hydrostat.	Calcu., Anal. &	Mech.	Cal., Anal. Mech.
Constr. of	Applied Mech.	Prac. Astron.	Descrip. Geo.
Mach.	Spher. Astron.	Geodesy—Trig.,	Railroad Surv.
Steam Eng.	Surv.—roads	railroad &	Shades, Shadows
Chem. Prep &	railroads &	mine surv.	Persj.
Org. Anal.	canals	Descrip. Geo.—	Physics
Indust. Org.	Descrip. Geo.—	persp., topograph.	Chemistry
Chem.	mason and carp.	draw., stereo.	
Mining	Physics	Indust. Physics	
Archit.	English	English	
Furnaces &	Drawing plans	Pract. Geo.	
Foundaries	etc.	Constr.—	
Tech. (Mills,	Foreign Lang.	theo. of struct.	
oil making,	Compute of earth	bridg., hydraul.,	
spining,	work and mason.	railways	
felting	Hydrograph. Surv.	Mining	
potteries etc.)		Metallurgy	
Railways		Philosophy of Mind.	

The curricula comparisons reveal a number of similarities and differences. Basically all curricula are three years in length, with that of the Ecole Centrale being strictly professional as compared with its American counterparts. The inclusion of technical courses resulted from the Ecole's unique organization, the preparation of its students, and the type of its faculty. The Ecole Centrale had no relation to the universities of France, its students were graduates of the Ecole Polytechnic and its curriculum was designed by professional engineers. In contrast, the American student was a product of the secondary school system, who completed a curriculum designed by college trained men who were basically college teachers with little if any experience in engineering. This difference will explain how the engineering school became attached to the college, and how the medical and law schools became practitioner schools appended to, but never fully controlled by, the colleges and universities to which they were attached. Actually, by copying much of the curriculum from France, with its professional character, it is possible that the American engineering schools adopted a more technical curriculum than had they evolved completely from American experiences.

Another apparent difference between the European and the various American curricula was the large amount of time devoted to the study of French and English in American schools. This is believed to have resulted from two factors. The first was the tradition of engineering curricula performing the college function of extending general education beyond the secondary school. The second factor was the scarcity of treatises and technical texts in the English language, with the resultant dependence on French publications. There is little to suggest that languages were studied for their humanistic and commercial values. In general it may be concluded that the American curricula could be described as offering a combination of general college and engineering science courses, with relatively few strictly professional subjects included.

Engineering Education in Colleges and Universities

Classification of Schools.—Rensselaer Polytechnic Institute was not only the first engineering school, but was also representative of one of the three types of engineering institutions that have developed in the United States. The type it represents includes those established by private beneficience for the sole purpose of supplying technical education. In this category are such institutions as the Massachusetts Institute of Technology, and the Illinois Institute of Technology.

A second type of engineering school, distinct in origin, is represented by schools attached more or less loosely to established colleges and universities. These schools are also privately supported and independent of state or government control. The early schools in this category include the scientific or engineering division of Union College, Harvard University, Yale University and Dartmouth College. The educational pattern, developed by the above named schools, was utilized to a great extent by the third type of engineering school. This third type includes those colleges, or schools of state universities and colleges, that receive their chief revenues from state or federal appropriations.

Union College.—From its beginning in 1795 this college was liberal in its organization and policies. Its charter provided that no one denomination of Christians could have a majority on the board of trustees: [17] hence the name Union. The administration of the college was unusual in having Eliphalet Nott (1773-1866) president for sixty-two years from 1804 to 1866. Schmidt in the following gives some interesting characteristics of Nott and the college he was president of:

> . . . Like Witherspoon and Dwight, Nott was a national figure, though in a different way. Before the end of his career he was widely known a a vigorous opponent of slavery and liquor, as a formidable financier, as the inventor of the first anthracite stove and the first steamboat to use coal for fuel, but primarily as the president of the most conspicuous "progressive" college of the first half of the nineteenth century. For much of his time Union was the second largest college in the country in enrollment, and in some years its graduating class was the largest, outstripping even Yale.[18]

Nott was enthusiastic concerning the future, and in his semi-centennial address of 1854 he stated that: ". . . The college also, liberalized and adapted to the wants of a young country and a progressive age, invites our youth to its consecrated halls."[19]

To meet this new challenge he discarded the classical curriculum by replacing Greek and Latin with modern languages in 1809 and by introducing a scientific course in 1828. Establishing the scientific course in 1828 is of special significance, because in 1829 Nott was appointed president of Rensselaer.[20] This was the year that has previously been mentioned as the time when Van Rensselaer signified his intention of discontinuing the school. Nott continued to act as president of both institutions until 1845, when he resigned as president of Rensselaer.[21] No special significance has been attached to his resignation in 1845, but it hardly appears a conincidence that this same year, when Nott had resigned as president of Rensselaer, Union College established a school of engineering.

[17] *First Semicentennial of Union College* (Schenectady, New York: W. C. Little and Company, 1845) p. 12.
[18] G. P. Schmidt, *op. cit.*, p. 112.
[19] G. Van Santword, *Memoirs of Eliphalet Nott* (New York, 1876) p. 324.
[20] P. C. Ricketts, *op. cit.*, p. 66.
[21] *Ibid.*, p. 92.

The preceding is presented because Union College as a pioneer in engineering education is either disregarded entirely or discussed but briefly and inadequately. Studies that omit mention of Union College are those by R. H. Thurston[22] in 1893, by C. R. Mann[23] in 1918 and by W. E. Wichenden[24] in 1929. A typical quotation giving an incorrect presentation of the status of Union College is the following statement by Wellington:

> During the next two years, however, three different schools, each of which has endured to the present day, were founded. The first was the School of Engineering of Union College, Schenectady, N.Y., founded in the United States but as the first ever founded by the enterprise of an existing classical school without any gift from a founder. Union College itself was founded in 1795, and was in the center of early engineering activity, the first canal work on this continent and the first railway work of any magnitude having been done in or near to Schenectady. To this fact, perhaps, rather than to any exceptional foresight or breadth of view, was owing its exceptionally early foundation. The school was rather a small affair up to 1860, however, sometimes graduating two or three engineers a year, and sometimes none. The first special degrees in engineering seem to have been given in 1875.[25]

In making these statements Wellington has disregarded the fact that canal building was at a standstill in New York state in 1845. He also neglects the prestige of Union College itself during this period and makes no mention of the place of Nott and his acquaintanceship with technical education. Union College in 1829 with its 233 students was the third largest college in the United States, being surpassed by Yale (324) and Harvard (254).[26] By 1859 Union was still important, and placed fifth among the following colleges: Yale (502), North Carolina (450), Virginia (417), Harvard (409), and Union (326).[27] During this same period Rensselaer had 75 students in 1842, 96 students in 1843, and as few as 35 students for the year 1845. With respect to the number of engineering graduates Union College did well, as the figures of Wellington in another article show that for the years 1850 to 1865 inclusive Union College graduated 40 civil engineers to the 88 that Rensselaer graduated.[28] In addition to these fifty engineers, and the fact that the first fraternities in the United States were founded at Union, the following summation by Fox indicates that its success and program can hardly be considered the result of mere chance:

[22] R. H. Thurston, op. cit., p. 925.
[23] C. R. Mann, op. cit., p. 5.
[24] W. E. Wickenden, op. cit., p. 814.
[25] A. M. Wellington, "Early Engineering Schools Following Rensselaer Polytechnic Institute," Engineering News (April 28, 1892) p. 433.
[26] American Almanac for 1830, "College Attendance Statistics for 1829-30," Boston, 1830.
[27] American Almanac for 1860, "College Attendance Statistics for 1858-59," Boston, 1860.
[28] A. M. Wellington, "The Supply and Demand of Engineering," Engineering News (Aug. 4, 1892) p. 114.

Union graduates found their way to every state and every continent in positions of trust and influence; the painful restraint of space prevents the rehearsal of a long list of great names. Under Dr. Nott's regime alone, Union sent forth men who were to become: a president of the United States; six cabinet secretaries; 13 United States Senators; 91 members of the House of Representatives; 12 governors; 49 important diplomats; about 200 judges; 40 missionaries; and 86 college presidents.[29]

Lawrence Scientific School.—The third engineering school in the United States was founded in 1847 as a branch of Harvard University. This school was made possible by an initial gift of $50,000 from Abbott Lawrence, a merchant manufacturer and builder. Although this was the largest gift ever given an American collge, Lawrence gave another $50,000 in 1850.[30] To these amounts Samuel Hopper[31] (1808-1875), a merchant, banker, and industrialist, added $50,000 in 1865 to establish chairs in geology and mining.

It is to be noted that these men, Lawrence and Hooper, were like Rensselaer, neither educators nor engineers, but men who saw the necessity of providing new educational facilities to produce the engineers needed by the expanding economy. Wickenden credits Horsford with inspiring Lawrence, while Morison states that the credit goes to Charles S. Storrow.[32] Horsford, a chemist, was a Rensselaer graduate who later studied in Germany prior to his appointment as Rumford Professor at the Lawrence Scientific School. Storrow (Harvard, 1829) also studied at the Ecole des Ponts et Chaussees before becoming chief engineer of the Boston and Lowell Railroad and of the Lawrence mills and water works. Either one or both of these men could well have inspired and assisted Lawrence in founding the school. It would appear that Lawrence had some assistance from an educator and engineer, since the letter of instructions accompanying his gift indicates rare educational and professional insight. The following quotations from this letter will clarify the proposed program.

> For several years I have seen and felt the pressing want in our community (and in the whole country) of an increased number of men educated in the practical sciences. Elementary education appears to be well provided for in Massachusetts. There is, however, a deficiency in the means for higher education in certain branches of knowledge. For an early classical education we have our schools and colleges. From thence the special schools of Theology, Law, Medicine, and Surgery receive the young men destined to those professions; and those who look to commerce as their employment pass to the counting house of the ocean. But where can we send those who intend to devote themselves to the practi-

---

[29] Dixon F. Fox, *Union College, An Unfinished History* (Schenectady, New York: Graduate Council Union College) p. 15.
[30] T. T. Read, *op. cit.,* p. 23.
[31] S. E. Morison, *Three Centuries of Harvard,* op. cit., p. 306.
[32] *Ibid.,* p. 276.

cal application of science? How educate our Engineers, our Miners, Machinists and Mechanics? Our country abounds in men of action. Hard hands are ready to work upon our hard materials; and where shall sagacious heads be taught to direct those hands?

I have thought that the three great practical branches to which a scientific education is to be applied amongst us are, 1st, Engineering; 2d, Mining, in its extended sense, including metallurgy; 3d, the invention and manufacture of machinery. These must be deemed kindred branches, starting from the same point, depending in many respects on the same principles, and gradually diverging to their more special applications. Mathematics, especially chemistry, the foundation of knowledge and an all-important study for the mining Engineer and the key to the processes by which the rude ore becomes the tenacious and ductile metal, Geology, Mineralogy, and the other sciences, investigating the properties and uses of materials employed in the arts, Carpentry, Masonry, Architecture and Drawing, are all studies which should be pursued to a greater or less extent in one of these principal divisions.

To carry out this source of education in its practical branches, there should be the most thorough instruction in Engineering, Geology, Chemistry, Mineralogy, Natural Philosophy, and Natural History. Chemistry is provided for, and in the last two branches, instruction might perhaps be given by the present College professors.

. . . Nor do I mean to occupy the ground of another branch of science that will, I suppose, at a future time, present strong claims upon the public bounty. I allude to Natural History, now in charge of that accomplished naturalist Dr. Gray. I wish to see all branches of science prosecuted with vigor, and moving forward in perfect harmony at Cambridge.[33]

In the parts quoted, and in the rest of this letter of instruction, Mr. Lawrence was unmistakably clear as to the kind of school he desired to found. What he wanted, and what the public needed, was a school of engineering for the teaching of engineering (civil), mining and metallurgy, and the invention and manufacture of machinery (mechanical engineering). He was also equally clear that natural history, natural philosophy, etc., should be taught by the regular Harvard professors and taught as they apply to the three great practical branches.

On the day the gift was received, the Corporation of Harvard College held a meeting and passed a vote of thanks to Mr. Lawrence containing the following statement:

. . . It is deemed by the Corporation a high privilege and a great reward for their labors, to be the stewards of such bounty: and they pledge their best efforts to carry faithfully into execution the enlightened suggestions with which the letter accompanying the donation is filled.[34]

On the basis of the above it was to be expected that the Lawrence Scien-

34 Vote by the Corporation of Harvard College, June 7, 1847, and signed by its secretary James Walker.

tific School would develop into the outstanding technical school for engineering in the United States. From its very beginning, however, the President and Corporation spoiled its chances by appointing to its faculty Louis Agassiz, an international figure from Switzerland, as professor of zoology and geology. For its first two years of operation, Professor Horsford, an eminent chemist, was the only other member of the faculty. The interests of these men lay in the directions of the pure sciences, and by their combined ability and enthusiasm they developed an outstanding school of pure science.

Despite the instructions of Mr. Lawrence, engineering was not taught at the Lawrence Scientific School until 1849, at which time Henry L. Eustis (1819-1885) was appointed professor of engineering. Eustis graduated in 1838 from Harvard and was first man in the class of 1842 at West Point. For two years he worked on the design and construction of a number of military projects and for two years prior to his Harvard appointment he taught at West Point. His salary was $3,000 per year and was paid from a combination of tuition fees and endowment income, as suggested in the following portion of the letter of instruction:

> . . . The professors in this school should depend to a considerable extent upon fees; it is the best guarantee of exertion and fidelity, and the permanent prosperity of the institution. I will therefore further suggest, that each of the above professors shall receive, after all ordinary expenses shall have been paid, one half of the tuition fees until they amount to a sum, annually, not exceeding three thousand dollars, including their stated salaries.[35]

The Lawrence Scientific School was not well organized as a cohesive unit, but consisted of small separate groups of which one was engineering. Until 1851 a diploma listing the courses completed was given, and from 1851 to 1871 the bachelor of science degree was awarded on the basis of an examination rather than the fullfilment of a prescribed group of courses. Although a minimum attendance of one year was required, the examination was usually passed after a residence of from 18 to 30 months. There were great differences of preparation among the students, as they were not required to pass the entrance examination for freshmen at Harvard College. These conditions placed considerable responsibility upon Eustis, who, for a period of over thirty years, carried on as the only professor of engineering on the staff. Morison described the organization in the following quotation:

> The work of instruction was conducted for the first 20 years on the assumption that the students were men of serious purpose who were preparing themselves for a professional career in some field of applied science. The choice of studies was optional with the students, subject to the approval of the faculty; and attendance at lectures was at first volun-

[35] Letter of instruction from Lawrence, op. cit.

tary, but later it was made compulsory. The method and scope of instruction varied among the several departments. In general each student spent most of his time in close personal relation with one teacher in one department with occasional lectures in allied subjects under other teachers.[36]

Morison, to illustrate how the general method applied to the teaching of engineering, gives the following excerpts from the Harvard catalogue of 1849-50 and 1850-51.

> *Engineering.*—Professor Eustis will receive special students to the course of instruction in Engineering, who will give their attendance at the school from 9 o'clock A.M. to 5 o'clock P.M. The course will include instruction in Descriptive Geometry, with its application to masonry and stone cutting, the construction of arches etc. The theory of shades, shadows, and perspectives, illustrated by a course of drawing and mapping in all its branches. Surveying with the use of instruments, and actual operations in the field. The nature and properties of building materials and their application to the construction of railroads, canals, bridges, etc.[37]

It is apparent that the above program was set up to train civil engineers on a very limited basis. Actually, no provision was made for mining engineering until 1865, and for mechanical engineering until an even later date. Thus it is evident that Mr. Lawrence's wishes were not complied with, and that the bright promise envisioned by his gifts and the letter of instruction were not realized. It should not be inferred from this, however, that in another light the Lawrence Scientific School was not a success. Actually Eustis was a good teacher, and Agassiz, Horsford and Gray were responsible for some outstanding graduates. It is a fact that up to 1866 the school had a total of 147 graduates of whom no less than 94 became professors or teachers and five became college presidents, including John Runkle of the Massachusetts Institute of Technology and Thomas Brown of Leheigh University. This record was outstanding, but was not consistent with Mr. Lawrence's wishes. Lawrence made no mention of teaching in the following excerpt from his letter of instruction:

> We have already in the United States a large body of young men who have received a classical education, many of whom find it difficult to obtain a livelihood in what are termed the learned professions. I believe the time has arrived when we should make an effort to diversify the occupations of our people, and develop more fully their strong mental and physical resources, throughout the Union.[38]

Of the 147 graduates, only 41[39] were engineers and their field of training was restricted to civil engineering. Mining engineering, metallurgy and me-

36 S. E. Morison, *Development of Harvard University,* op. cit., p. 416.
37 *Ibid.,* p. 419.
38 A. Lawrence to S. Elliot, *op. cit.*
39 M. A. Worthington, *op. cit.*

chanical engineering were not taught as requested by the donor, with the result that Harvard missed the opportunity of developing the first comprehensive engineering school in the United States. It has been stated that had the Lawrence Scientific School realized its opportunity, Massachusetts Institute of Technology would not have been founded. Wickenden, for instance, thought so:

> . . . Harvard's tardiness in realizing Lawrence's intentions appears to have been a major factor contributing to the establishment of the Massachusetts Institute of Technology as an independent foundation in 1860.[49]

The fact is, however, that William Rogers, who later founded Massachusetts Institute of Technology, and his brother Henry were planning a school in Boston before the Lawrence Scientific School was launched. A portion of a letter written by Henry to his brother William concerning the possibility of establishing a polytechnic school as a branch of the Lowell Institute substantiates this point.

> . . . Mr. Lowell will, I hope organize such a branch of his institute; and if he does not, you and I can surely get one founded here by going about it in the right way. Let us give this matter our earnest and sober thought, remembering that if I get the profesorship in Harvard it will rather promote the plan than mar it.[41]

After the Lawrence Scientific School had started, but before it had an opportunity to show the direction it was finally to take, William Rogers was still determined to found a school as the following letter indicates:

> . . . The more I think of our plan of a Polytechnic School, the more confident I feel of its rapid and great success. The Lawrence School never can succeed on its present plan of accomplishment of what was intended. It can only, as now organized, draw a small number of the body of students aside from the usual college routine. It should be in reality a school of applied science, embracing at least four professorships, and it ought to be in a great measure independent of the other departments of Harvard. Besides, Cambridge is not the place for such a school. It should be in Boston.[42]

The Lawrence Scientific School did not develop into the school its founder envisioned for it, because the president and corporation of the Harvard college did not follow his instructions and not because of other institutions that were later founded in the area. During this period of definition prior to the Civil War, Lawrence continued giving degrees on an examination basis. A curriculum that was co-ordinated with that of the college and similar to the

[40] Wickenden, *op. cit., p.* RVD.
[41] Henry Rogers to William Rogers, March 8, 1846.
[42] William Rogers to Henry Rogers, October 3, 1847.

pattern of engineering studies used by other colleges in liberal arts environments did not develop until 1871.

The Sheffield Scientific School.—The Sheffield Scientific School of Yale, the fourth engineering school in the United States, is said by Mann,[43] Thurston,[44] and Wellington[45] to have been founded in 1847. Actually the engineering school was erected in 1852 within the department of Philosophy and Arts. This department was founded in 1847 by the following resolution of the Yale Corporation:

> 1. There shall be a fourth department of instruction for other than undergraduate students, who are not in the departments of theology, medicine and law, to be called the Department of Philosophy and the Arts. The department is intended to embrace philosophy, literature, history and moral sciences other than theology, the natural sciences excepting medicine, and their application to the arts.
> 2. Instruction in this department may be given by professors not belonging to the department, by professors in the academical departments, and by such others as the president and fellow members may approve. But no second course of lectures on the same branch may be given without the consent of the previous lecturer.
> 3. All graduates of this or other colleges, and all other young men of fair moral character, may be allowed to pursue such studies included in this department as they may desire. But dismissed students from this or other colleges and undergraduate students, without express leave of the academical faculty, shall not enjoy the privileges of this department.
> 4. The instructor in this department may make such arrangements as respects remuneration for their instructions, as they may think proper.[46]

For the first five years of its existence this department was, for all practical purposes, a school of applied chemistry carried on by the personal efforts of Professors John P. Norton and Benjamin Silliman Jr. Both these men had been students of Professor Benjamin Silliman Sr. and were well qualified for their positions. Norton had studied for two years in Europe following his graduation from Yale, while Silliman Jr. had remained on as his father's assistant. The department was a private enterprise, in the sense that the professors paid the corporation one hundred and fifty dollars a year for the use of a house that served as a chemical laboratory, and that the only salary they received was that obtained from tuition fees. Only an average of fifteen students were in attendance during the first few years,[47] and these students were not enrolled in the college nor did they receive a degree upon completing the course. The instruction was very informal, with the exception of two formal

---

[43] C. R. Mann, *op. cit.,* p. 5.
[44] Rit Thurston, *op. cit.,* p. 926.
[45] A. M. Mann, *op. cit.,* Aug. 4, 1892, p. 114.
[46] Russell H. Chittenden, *History of Sheweld Scientific School* (New Haven, Conn.: Yale Univrsity Press, 1928) p. 41.
[47] *Ibid.,* p. 47.

lecture courses. One of these courses on agricultural chemistry was taught by Norton in the second term, and the other on chemistry applied to manufacturing and mineralogy by Silliman in the third term.

After this five year trial period, two important changes took place. In 1852 the Corporation established the degree of Bachelor of Philosophy, to be given by the Department of Philosophy and Arts, provided the student was 21 years of age, had resided at the college two years and had successfully passed an examination embracing at least three branches of study. In the same year there was established a school of engineering within the Department of Philosophy and Arts. The school of engineering came into being when the Corporation accepted the proposal of Professor William A. Norton contained in the following letter:

> I propose to open a School of Engineering, sustain it at my own expense, and provide it with the necessary apparatus;—receiving all the emoluments of the same. The School to be attached to the Department of Philosophy and the Arts in the College, to have all the privileges incident to this relation, and a Professorship of Engineering to be instituted.
>
> The plan will be essentially the same as that of the School of Engineering organized by me two years since in Brown University, which met with good success,—the number of students increasing, by the beginning of the second year, to nineteen. It will also be similar to that of the Harvard School, the success of which is well known. Some modifications will, however, be introduced, which have been suggested by the experience of the last two years.
>
> The Course of Instruction will embrace the following studies and exercises.
>
> Surveying, in all its branches, with the use and adjustment of instruments, theodolite, compass, level, etc.; and daily operations in the field for a period of two months or more.
>
> A complete course of Drawing; topographical, geometrical, machine, architectural; with shading and tinting. The exercises in drawing to continue several hours each day, and to extend through the first year, or the greater part of it.
>
> Descriptive Geometry—Geometrical theory of shades and shadows—Linear Perspective—Isometrical Perspective: instruction to be given in these branches, (which embrace the complete doctrine of Projections), in connection with systematic exercises in geometrical drawing.
>
> Applications of descriptive Geometry to Masonry and Stonecutting, in the Construction of Arches, &c, and to Civil and Mechanical Engineering.
>
> The Principles of Architecture.
>
> Analytical Geometry and Differential and Integral Calculus.
>
> Mechanics, including Hydraulics and Pneumatics:—Application of Mechanics to Machinery and Engineering.
>
> The Science of Construction in all its departments; with a discussion of the nature, strength and mode of preparation of building materials.

Field-engineering; or the location of roads, surveys for excavations and embankments, for the determination of time, latitude and longitude, &c.

Students to be admitted to pursue either a full or partial course, at their option.

The period of time required to complete the full course about two years . . . .

1852.

(signed W. A. Norton)[48]

In connection with the above letter, Professor Silliman Sr. informed the Corporation that Professor Norton would not expect any appropriation of college funds. As a result, Profesor Norton received no salary other than tuition, which amounted to thirty dollars a term or ninety dollars a year. This practice was quite in contrast to that at Harvard, where the professors received three thousand dollars a year.

The qualifications of Profesor Norton were excellent. He graduated from West Point in 1831 and had twenty-one years of teaching experience before going to Yale. This experience consisted of two years at West Point, six years at the University of the City of New York, eleven years at Delaware College and two years at Brown University. His experience at Brown University could well have been the reason for his desire to establish an Engineering school at Yale. This is explained in the following interesting quotation taken from Bronson's *History of Brown University:*

> In January the President conferred with the Executive Board on the 'insubordination of the last term,' and laid it chiefly to the lack of unanimity, in the Faculty about the enforcement of discipline. A committee having confirmed his opinion, the board voted that it was "expedient" that Mr. Green and Professors Porter and Norton "should terminate their connection with the University!" The three resigned forthwith.[49]

The above statement could well explain why Norton went to Yale as well as why 19 students transferred to Yale from Brown. In defense of Norton it should be stated that he was very effective at Yale and taught there for thirty-years.

It will be noted that the program at Yale, like the one at Harvard, envisioned a professional school of applied science to be rather loosely connected with the University as were the schools of Law, Medicine, and Theology. Norton's course of instruction was completely professional without any tie-in with the college. In this same connection it is of interest that for the school year 1852-53, of the 55 students enrolled in the department of Philosophy and Arts, 16 were college graduates. In addition, when the school of engineering

[48] Russell Henry Chittenden, *History of the Sheweld Scientific School of Yale University* 184-1922 (New Haven: Yale University Press, 1928) pp. 57-58.
[49] W. C. Bronson, *op. cit.*, p. 296.

at Yale instituted the degree of Civil Engineering in 1859, it required that to be eligible for the degree the students must previously have received the Bachelor of Philosophy degree.

From 1852 the engineering school developed in an effort to keep pace with the rapidly changing industrial economy. In 1855 the Department of Philosophy and Arts became the Yale Scientific School and expanded the engineering by establishing a chair of metallurgy. To this position Mr. George Busch was appointed, giving Yale the opportunity of becoming the outstanding school of metallurgy in the country. George Busch had an exceptionally good background, consisting of graduation from Yale in 1852, one year at Munich, one year at the Royal Mining School at Freiberg and one year at the Royal School of Mines in London. According to Read, Busch was the best qualified man in the country, but aside from giving some public lectures was never able to teach metallurgy at Yale.[50] This happened because there were no students interested in the subject; so that Yale, a pioneer in the field ahead of its time, had to make a fresh start in metallurgy, fifty years later.

In 1856 a proposed reorganization, as we have mentioned, restated the idea of a true professional school. In addition, it opened the door for general studies to be supplied by the college. This gave a beginning to the final form of combination college and professional school that was eventually to evolve. Excerpts from the plan will illustrate this point:

> Such a school, forming, as it naturally would, a distinct department in the established system of education, may advantageously be connected like the law, medical and theological schools, with a complete university organization.
>
> It is believed that two classes of students shall desire to avail themselves of the advantages of the School of Science, those who aim to fit themselves for the practical pursuits of mining, engineering, agriculture, manufacturing, and the like without pursuing a college course, and also those who, having graduated, are disposed to pursue their scientific studies. To both such classes the school will be open . . . . As it is presumed that those who follow this three year's course will desire not only to be fitted for particular occupations but to become well educated men, provision is also made in the second or third years for instruction in various branches of general knowledge, attention to some of which it is proposed to require of all candidates for the degree of Bachelor of Philosophy.[51]

Whether or not a true professional school developed depended on which of the two classes of students previously referred to was considered. Those who already had a college course were well prepared to take a strictly professional training as originally outlined by Norton. For those limited to a common school education, the above aim of supplementing professional train-

[50] T. T. Read, op. cit., p. 24.
[51] R. H. Chittenden, op. cit., p. 67-68.

ing with a general education program was necessary. This point is emphasized because the difference between the legal, medical, and theological schools, on the one hand, and the engineering school on the other, stems directly from which of these two classes of students is catered to.

The above question was solved rather definutely for engineering education in the period following the civil war. In the meantime, Yale up to 1859 continued to develop its Scientific School without any adequate building or definite means of paying current expenses or professors salaries. In that year Mr. Joseph Sheffield provided a building and an additional fund of $50,000 for the maintenance of the professorships of chemistry, metallurgy, and engineering. Mr. Sheffield, who had been active in railway construction throughout the country, recognized, as did Mr. Lawrence, the need for education in the applied sciences. Mr. Sheffield had another and more personal interest in the school, since Professor John A. Porter of the Scientific School had married one of his doughters. The gift of Mr. Sheffield gave permanence to Yale's program, and in 1861 the school assumed the title of Sheffield Scientific School. In the face of the many hardships that the program endured in its early years, there were 30 graduates up to the year 1866, as compared with 41 for Harvard, 46 for Union College and 124 for Rensselaer. This number appears small but it is significant for it indicates that the engineeriing program was permanently established at Yale, and that the Sheffield Scientific School played a significant part in the development of engineering education in the United States.

Chandler Scientific School.—The fifth engineering school in the United States was named after its founder and established as a part of Dartmouth College in 1851. The school was made possible by the sum of $50,000 bequeathed to the College by Abiel Chandler (1778-1851) of Walpole, New Hampshire. Chandler had graduated from Harvard in 1806 and for many years was a successful merchant in Boston. At the time of his death he was a widower without children. Like Rensselaer and Lawrence, he was neither an engineer nor educator, and also like them he gave a letter of instruction specifying the type of school he wanted established. One clause of his will pertaining to the instruction to be given runs as follows:

In the practical or useful arts of life composed chiefly in the branches of mechanics and civil engineering, the invention and manufacture of machinery, carpentry, masonry, architecture and drawing, the investigation of the properties and uses of the materials employed in the arts, the modern languages and English literature, together with bookkeeping and other branches of knowledge as may best qualify young persons for the duties and employment of active life: but first of all and above all I would enjoin in connecteion with the above branches the careful inculcation of the principles of pure morality, piety and religion without introducing the topics of controversial theology, that the benefits of said department of schol may be equally enjoyed by all religious denominations without distinction. No other or higher preparatory studies are to be required in order to enter said department or school than are pursued in the common schools of New England.[52]

Some of the wording in the above clause is exactly that used by Abbott Lawrence, in his letter of instruction, when he founded the Lawrence Scientific School. In addition to this indication of Candler's knowledge of the Lawrence Scientific School, it could also be that he was aware that Lawrence's plan was not being carried out at Harvard. This seems to be implied in the provision of his will creating a board of visitors who were to pick their successors and periodically to see that the terms of his will were being carried out.

The Chandler Scientific School opened in 1851 with all the instruction given by regular members of the Dartmouth faculty, who received extra pay for their services. The school granted a bachelor of science degree for a three-year course, and in the first year had seventeen students. The number gradually increased to 42 in 1863 and to 70 in 1869. Attempts to hold some of the classes in common with those of the college were unsuccessful. This resulted in a duplication of much of the teaching effort, which created a real problem due to small classes in both the college and scientific school. The college enrollment in 1863 was 161 students and that of the Chandler School was 42.[53]

To give direction to the program, Professor S. Woodman, a mathematics professor in the college, was made Professor of Civil Engineering in the Chandler School, a position he held as the only full-time faculty member until 1863. Under his direction, the course in 1867 was increased to four years and a new curriculum was instituted. Richardson describes this curriculum as follows:

> . . . It provided in the first years for instruction in mathematics, natural science, modern languages, and graphics, with a small amount of English, history, moral science, political economy and the like. In the fourth year some of these general subjects were continued by all students, but a portion of the time was devoted to a selection from civil engineering, commercial subjects, or English literature and intellectual philosophy, the first introduction of the elective principle into the curriculum of the college.[54]

The above curriculum shows that even though the Chandler Scientific School was an organization distinct from the college, the distinction was more in name than in practice. The professors from the college taught the liberal arts subjects, with the result that in the final outcome the program was one that coordinated general education with professional courses in engineering and commerce. The number of graduates from this program was small, num-

[52] L. B. Richardson, op. cit., p. 422. (Vol. 1).
[53] Ibid., p. 516 (Vol. 2).
[54] Ibid., p. 424 (Vol. 1).

bering only 18 up to 1866. The school did, however, establish the earliest four-year program that was definitely built upon a common school education. In addition, it established applied science in one of the earliest liberal-arts colleges. Dartmouth was to later found a graduate school of engineering under the sponsorship of Thayer of West Point, a Dartmouth alumnus.

The University of Michigan.—In 1855 the engineering department of the University of Michigan was organized as the sixth engineering school in the United States that is still in existence. It was the first such school to be established in a state-supported university, and was the product of the advanced thinking of President Henry Tappan, who in his inaugural address of December 1852 proposed:

> A Scientific course parallel to the classical course containing, besides other branches, Civil Engineering, Astronomy with the use of an observatory, and the application of Chemistry and other Sciences to Agriculture and the Industrial Arts generally.[55]

President Tappan graduated from Union College in 1825 under Eliphalet Nott, who has previously been referred to as one of the most progressive educators of his time. In addition to teaching experience at the University of the City of New York, Tappan had made a study of the educational system of Germany. He was one of a large group who sought to reorganize the American college into a model of the German University. This movement was strong for the fifty years between 1825 and 1875 and was sponsored by such men as Ticknor, Bancroft, and Eliot of Harvard, Folwell of Minnesota, James of Illinois, White of Cornell, Gilman of John Hopkins, and Hall of Clark University. The following statements from Tappan illustrate some of the thinking associated with this movement:

> We find the want of universities; hence, we are continually struggling to give our colleges as much of a university character as possible . . .
> Our Colleges grasp at a university amplitude of studies, at university capacities and functions, and take the name of universities, and yet universities they cannot be within the prescribed limits, with the general paucity of learned material and appliances, and while offering themselves as institutions for students in the elementary course. They were elementary schools of a higher grade in their inception, such they have ever continued to be, as such their existence will ever be demanded, and as such they require to be perfected. By retaining their original designation, while endeavoring to graft upon them what belongs properly to a university, we have only embarrassed them in their proper and possible functions, given them an equivocal character, and lessened their usefulness.[56]
> A German University is, therefore, an association of scholars for sci-

[55] W. A. Donnelly, *The University of Michigan* (Ann Arbor, Michigan: University of Michigan Press) Vol. III, p. 1161, (1953).
[56] Henry P. Tappan, *University Education* (New York Putnam Company, 1851) p. 78.

entific and educational purposes, as truly as the scholastic Universities; but as much in advance of the latter, as the modern world is in advance of the Middle Ages in general intelligence and useful improvements. We find here renewed, the freedom, the spirit, the ideal conception of the Greek schools; we find preserved in full energy the organization of the scholastic Universities; but, in addition to this, we find the modern University placed in its proper relation as the culmination of a grand system of Education. The good of the past is preserved, the evils are eliminated, the imperfections are supplied, and the unity of all true progress is demonstrated.[57]

To produce such a change implied the creation of a new type of institution or an extension of the high-school system. In his inaugural address in 1869, Folwell of Minnesota gave the following proposal, which was one of many statements of that time that later would be used as a justification of the Junior College.

> . . . those studies which now form the body of work for the first two years in our ordinary American Colleges. It is a clear case that such a transposition must by and by be made . . . How great the gain . . . if a youth could remain at the high school or academy, residing in his home, until he had reached a point, say somewhere near the end of the sophomore year, there to go over all those studies which as a boy he ought to study, under tutors and governors! Then let the boy, grown up to be a man, emigrate to the university, there to enter upon the work of a man . . . .[58]

The above statements are offered to show that a force was at work that could have been responsible for a truly professional course of engineering studies. Had these men been successful, the Lawrence, the Sheffield and the Chandler schools could have developed into institutions similar to our present theological, law, and medical schools. Tappan attempted to organize the University in this new fashion, but had difficulties with his board of regents and was forced to resign in 1863.

With respect to engineering, the scientific course announced in the Michigan catalogue of 1852-53 included civil engineering in the third and fourth years. The first degree was awarded in 1857. In 1855 a curriculum leading to the degree of civil engineer was announced and described in the catalogue of 1855-56. This course included Mathematics, Graphics, Physics, Natural Science, Elements of Astronomy, Language, Philosophy and the following engineering subjects: Plane Geodetics, Railroad and Mining Surveying, Leveling, Nature and Strength of Materials, Theory of Construction, Architecture, Machines (particularly the steam engine) and Motors (Steam and

[57] Henry P. Tappan, "Progress of Educational Development in Europe," *Barnard's American Journal of Education,* Vol. 1, pp. 266-267.
[58] W. W. Folwell, *University Addresses* (Minneapolis, Minn.: H. W. Wilson Co., 1909) p. 37-38.

Water). It was stated that the entire course could be accomplished by the industrious student in four years but that a longer time could be devoted to it with profit.

During these years the engineering school at the University of Michigan had two very competent professors who later became famous in their professions. For the first two years, from 1855 to 1857, William Peck, a West Point graduate of 1844, was professor of civil engineering. In 1857 he became professor of Mathematics, Mechanics and Astronomy at Columbia University's School of Mines, where he remained until he died in 1892. Peck was replaced by DeWolsen Wood, a Rensselaer graduate who walked from Detroit to Ann Arbor on the chance there was a teaching position open. Wood remained at Michigan until 1872, at which time he went to Stevens Institute of Technology. The problem of the length and type of engineering curriculum was of concern to Wood but he never arrived at a satisfactory answer to the following question: "Should the entire (engineering) course be included in point of time wthin the present undergraduate course of four years or should a fifth University year be added to complete the course?"[59]

The above question was not answered by those who followed Tappan and Wood at Michigan. The engineering school, however, continued to grow, until by 1890 it graduated a total to that date of 360 engineers, being second in number only to Rensselaer and the Sheffield School.

School of Mines of Columbia University. — The School of Mines of Columbia University was the seventh engineering school founded and had many characteristics different from the six previously described institutions. The major differences are: 1) it is the first mining and metallurgical school still in existence, 2) it is the first technical school to have been planned, organized, founded, and operated by a trained engineer. Although its original purpose was to train mining and metallurgical engineers, it was from its early days a general school of technology, using the basic courses necessary for a mining and metallurgical curriculum as the core for the study of other branches of engineering.

Nowithstanding the above differences, this school had many features in common with the existing institutions. By being attached to an established college, and by being founded without any special endowment, it had much in common with the engineering school of Union College. It resembled the Sheffield Scientific School by requiring that the total faculty expenses be covered by tuition fees. Like the Lawrence, the Sheffield, and the Chandler School, the School of Mines of Columbia University was set up as a separate school, using some of the facilities of the college but independent as far as entrance requirements, length of course and curriculum were concerned.

[59] W. A. Donnelly, *op. cit.,* p. 1163.

The founder of the School of Mines was Thomas Egleston, who gradua-ted from Yale in 1854 prior to being an assistant to Professor Silliman Jr. In 1860 Egleston graduated from the Ecole des Mines, and became interested in making it possible for Americans to receive the same training at home that many were going to Europe to obtain.[60] (Read lists twenty-five Americans who had studied at the Ecole des Mines and seventy-four who had studied at the Mining Academy at Freiburg[61] prior to 1856.)

Egleston's plan of study was contained in a 1,500 word outline presen-ted to the trustees of Columbia. This outline contained the following:

> To furnish the student the means of acquiring a thorough scientific and practical knowledge of those branches of science which relate to mining and the working up of the mineral resources of this country, and to supply to those engaged in mining and metallurgical operations, per-sons competent to take charge of new and old works, and conduct them on thoroughly scientific principles.[62]

To accomplish the above he organized a three-year course of study re-quiring algebra, plane geometry, and plane trigonometry for entrance. At a later period in 1858, a preparatory year was organized which was eventually made the first year of a four-year course.[63] In thus absorbing a preparatory program Columbia was similar to Rensselaer and Yale in the development of its four year curriculum. The only degree offered was that of mining engineer, but as Columbia developed into a comprehensive technical school, degrees in civil engineering, architecture, electrical and mechanical engineering were ad-ded.

One of the outstanding characteristics of the school was the faculty that Egleston attracted to work with him without any guarantee of salary other than student tuitions. In addition to Egleston, there were Chandler from Har-vard and Gottingen Universities, Vinton from West Point and the Ecole des Mines, Newberry from Paris, Joy from Gottingen, in addition to William Peck, who graduated from West Point and had previously taught at the Uni-versity of Michigan. To these men Chandler gave leadership after the original organization by Elgeston. Under this outstanding faculty the success of the school was immediate, with the result that in its second year of operation it had half as many students as the college had acquired in over a century of existence.[64] Church supplied more details regarding the size of the student body in the initial years.

---

[60] Daniel S. Martin, "Sketch of Thomas Egleston," *Popular Science Monthly* (1899) Vol. 55, p. 257.

[61] T. T. Read, *op. cit.*, p. 27-28.

[62] George F. Kunz, *Biographical Notes of Thomas Egleston*, (New York: American Insti-tute of Mining Engineering, 1902) Vol. 31, p. 5-20.

[63] *Columbia University* (1754-1904) (New York: Columbia University Press, 1904) p. 357.

[64] T. T. Read, *op. cit.*, p. 51.

It was thought that the school would be considered fairly established if twelve students presented themselves. The number was twenty on the opening day, and before the year was out nearly fifty young men had joined. The next year a building for laboratories, collections, and lecture rooms was ready, and the number of students was about ninety, increasing to one-hundred and thirty the third year.[65]

During its first five years the Columbia School developed into a general school of technology, and from this beginning has been a continued leader in the field of engineering education in both the type of educational organization it has developed and in the contribution of its graduates.

Massachusetts Institute of Technology. — The establishment of this school by the efforts of William and, to a lesser degree, Henry Rogers was the result of a promotional program that extended over a period of fifteen years. When the Institute was finally incorporated in 1861, the combined support of labor, industry, and the general public had been secured. In this respect it has been termed the first engineering school "organized as a result of a popular movement and a general sense of need, and not as the result either of a gift from an individual or of state laws in aid of it."[66] This special characteristic justifies a description of its development. The actual educational program is not considered, since the combined effects of financial problems and the civil war delayed its final opening until 1865.

Henry Rogers visited Boston in 1846 with the hope of securing the Rumford Professorship at Harvard. Having other ambitions as well, he approached the trustees of the Lowell Institute concerning the possibility of establishing a technological school in conjunction with their institution. In the following parts of a letter from his brother William he discusses this situation:

> But I have to speak of another interesting matter, Mr. Lowell, with whom I have been talking, after mentioning the features in the Lowell will which enjoins the creation of classes in the Institute to receive exact instructions in useful knowledge, requested me to give him in writing the views I had just been unfolding of the value of a School of Arts as a branch to the Lowell Institute. My communication to the corporation has, I am sure, made an impression on him, and it is possible he has seen, by what is there stated, the importance of teaching science in its applied forms in this community . . . . At no distant day, if not indeed soon, Mr. Lowell will, I hope, organize such a branch in his institute: and if he does not, you and I can surely get one founded here by going about it in the right way. Let us give this matter our earnest and sober thoughts, remembering that if I get the professorship in Harvard, it will rather promote the plan than mar it.[67]

[65] John A. Church, "Mining Schools in the United States," *North American Review,* Vol. CXIII (Boston, 1871) p. 79.
[66] A. M. Wellington, "The Massachusetts Institute of Technology," *The Engineering News*
[67] Letter from Henry Rogers to William Rogers March 8, 1846, *Life and Letters* of W.B. *Rogers* (Boston: Houghton Mufflin and Co., 1896) Vol. I, p. 256.

In response to the above letter William Rogers replied with a proposal that turned out to be the Magna Carta for the school and is called "A Plan for a Polytechnic School in Boston." The important parts of this plan, taken from his letter, are as follows:

A school of practical science completely should, I conceive, embrace full courses of instruction in all the principles of physical truth having direct relation to the art of constructing machinery, the application of motive power, manufactures, mechanical and chemical, the art of engraving with electrotype and photography, mineral exploration and mining, chemical analysis, engineering, locomotive and agriculture . . .

The true and only practical object of a polytechnic school is, as I conceive, the teaching not of minute details and manipulations of the arts, which can be done only in the workshops, but the inculcation of those scientific principles which form the basis of the explanation of them and along with this, full and methodical review of all their leading processes and operations in connection with physical power.

A polytechnic school, therefore, duly organized, has in view an object of the utmost practical value, and one which in such a community as that of Boston could not fail of being realized in the amplest degree.[68]

The hope of Henry Rogers that the Lowell Institute trustees would adopt this plan faded when it became evident that provisions in the Lowell will made it impossible to use its funds for a school such as the Rogers brothers proposed. From this point on the further efforts to continue the project were carried on by William Rogers alone since Henry did not receive the appointment at Harvard and a few years later accepted a professorship at Glasgow University in Scotland. The establishment of the Lawrence Scientific and the Sheffield School in 1847 did not discourage William Rogers, who was firm in his belief that the type of school he had in mind should be free and independent and not connected with any of the existing colleges.

In 1859, thirteen years after the initial effort was made, a new opportunity presented itself, described by Prescott:

. . . As Boston grew, more land was needed. The broad, shallow basin of the Charles River known as the Back Bay was one of the areas from which new land was gradually being created; and in 1859 Governor Banks, in his message to the legislature, pointed out that the opportunity was favorable to use this property for 'such public education improvement as will keep the name of the commonwealth forever green in the memory of her children.' Here at last, came a smile from opportunity.[69]

In accordance with this suggestion a group was organized that petitioned the legislature for a reservation of the State land in the Back Bay. The first two such petitions, one bearing Dr. Rogers' name and the second prepared by

---

[68] *Ibid.,* Letter of William Rogers to Henry Rogers, 1846 (Vol. 1) p. 420.
[69] Samuel C. Prescott, *When MIT Was Boston Tech* 1861-1916 (Cambridge: The Technology Press, 1954) p. 27.

him, were unsuccessful. In the meantime William Rogers was hoping for an appointment at Harvard as a letter to his brother Henry indicates:

> . . . Some days ago Hillard showed me part of a letter just arrived from Fulton, now you know, President of Harvard, in which he expresses the strong wish of himself and others to have me in Cambridge. They are proposing to establish a Professorship of Geology and Mining in connection with the Lawrence School . . .
> Probably no final steps will be taken in this matter for two or three months. Hillard thinks they would not offer a less salary than $1,500, that I should be able to continue to reside in Boston.[70]

The position referred to never materialized, and William, like his brother Henry was never offered a position on the Harvard faculty. In October of 1860 Rogers, heading a group of four, presented a third plan to the legislature, which was approved by the legislative committee. This report was entitled "Objects and Plan for an Institute of Technology, including a Society of Arts, a Museum of Arts, and a School of Industrial Science, proposed to be established in Boston." An act of incorporation was immediately prepared and successfully passed both senate and house, owing to the joint support of the Board of Trade, the American Academy of Arts and Sciences, the Society of Natural History, the New England Society for the Promotion of Manufacturers, and the State Teachers Associations. On April 10, 1861, Governor Andrew approved the "Act to Incorporate the Massachusetts Institute of Technology" and the fifteen-year program of the Rogers brothers was successful.

The structure of the newly formed institution was unique in that it contained three distinct divisions catering to the interests of those who supported its establishment. Though intended to provide a variety of public services, its name rapidly became identified with the work of what was originally to be the School of Industrial Science. The Society of Arts, sponsoring discussions and publications of popular interests, was active from the start. It was given separate corporate status subsidiary to the Institute, but had its own officers, constitution and by-laws. The Museum of Arts was never established.

Financial difficulties and the Civil War delayed the start of actual instruction until February 1865. In the intervening period William Rogers spent his time in organizing the institution in the duties of a new position that was created for him as described in the following letter to his brother Henry:

> I have now to tell you of a matter about myself that will surprise you. By a bill of the last Legislature a new office has been created, called the Inspector of Gas Meters and Illuminating Gas for the State, who is, as it were, to stand between the consumers and the gas companies. The salary's $3,000. The Governor some weeks ago, consulted me about it,

70 Letter of William Rogers to Henry Rogers, March 30, 1860, *op. cit.*,

asking me to accept the office. This I refused, urging the superior qualifications of Hayes, and my own inexperience in business matters. Since,
some days ago, I saw by the papers that he and the council had appointed me . . .
     I felt it was my duty to reconsider the decision . . .[71]

The salary, which was twice what he expected to receive from the Harvard appointment, enabled him to live well and develop his plans for a broad
curriculum, containing many separate technical courses that his original plan
had described in general. This he did in practically the back yard of the Lawrence Scientific School which had been founded to do almost the very thing
that William Rogers eventually accomplished.

The Missing School—The Polytechnic College of Pennsylvania

Introduction. — In addition to the schools just considered, there were
many private, state and national proposals for teaching applied science, agriculture and engineering. One such private venture was the attempt in 1852 to
establish at Albany, New York, a University to teach Science, Engineering,
Architecture, Mathematics, Geology, Mining and Metallurgy.[72] Another private attempt was the granting of a charter in 1858 by the New York legislature for the founding of the American School of Mines.[73] This school, whose
purposes were to develop the mineral wealth of the United States, included
such supporters as Peter Cooper, but for some unknown reason it never did
operate. The New York State Agricultural College was organized in 1853 to
teach theoretical and practical agriculture and engineering but the school
never opened owing to its poor financial structure and the sudden death of
its leading organizer, Delafield.[74] One national attempt of interest was that of
Charles Fleishman in 1838, who desired congress to establish practical colleges.[75] Another national attempt was that of the Illinois legislature, which at
the insistence of the industrial league, sponsored a proposed law in congress
in 1854 to give each state $500,000 to establish a university for the practical
education of the industrial classes.[76]

     An extended discussion of the above and similar attempts at founding
new schools of a technical nature would support the contention that the relatively few schools that were actually founded were not the measure of the true
social demand for a new type of institution to meet the needs of the country's
expanding industrial economy. A more detailed analysis would also show
that training in agriculture and engineering was considered the work of a
single school, and that proposals for such schools were a product of prosper-

[71] Letter from William Rogers to Henry Rogers, June 25, *op. cit.*
[72] Thomas T. Read, *op. cit.,* p. 41.
[73] *Ibid.,* p. 40.
[74] Transactions of the New York State Agricultural Society, 1853, p. 529-536.
[75] H. R. Cos. No. 334, 26 Congress, 2 Session Cultivalor VI, 1839.
[76] E. D. Rox, *op. cit.,* p. 44.

ity, because there was little or no interest in them during the depression years of 1837 and 1857.

During the mid-century period of strong interest, there was established the Polytechnic College of Pennsylvania. This deserves special consideration because of its organizational structure, and because also that it is so little known, although it was in existence for at least twenty-five years. Apart from a letter to the editor of the *Engineering News* on March 10, 1892 by Dan Cathcart of the class of 1857,[77] and another on August 25, 1892 by Hiram Stifer[78] of the class of 1876, the writer has found only one other reference made to this school by any of the writers on engineering education. This second reference was by Read, who describes briefly the school's mining curriculum. The two letters to the editor referred to were written for the purpose of asking why their school had been omitted from a list of the engineering schools of the nineteenth century. The editor replied as follows:

> We have no knowledge, of this institution other than that given in our correspondent's letter. It is in none of the lists of the Bureau of Education as far as we have discovered.[79]

The Charter and School's Establishment.—The Polytechnic College of Pennsylvania was granted its charter on April 5, 1853 by sections two to eight inclusive of a law enacted by the Senate and House of Representatives of the Pennsylvania General Assembly.[80] The trustees named in the original charter numbered twenty-seven and represented twelve counties and the city of Philadelphia. They were empowered to grant degrees and gave as their object "the education of youth in the arts, science, languages, and literature, particularly mining engineering, and the natural sciences, in their application to the arts and manufactures . . . ."[81]

The driving force behind the college was Dr. Alfred L. Kennedy, who remained president throughout the life of the institution. After the preliminary organization in 1851 and before its charter was granted in 1853, Kennedy began an inspection of the Polytechnic Institutions of Europe with the following result:

> After an absence of a year, he repeated the results of his visit, recommending that no one foreign institution be accepted as a model for the college, but that a plan be adopted based upon both the German and the French methods, viz: Those practiced at Carlsruhe in the Polytechnischen, and at Paris in L'Ecole Centrale des Arts—which recommendation was approved.[82]

77 Letter to the Editor, *Engineering News,* Nov. 10, 1892, p. 438.
78 Letter to the Editor, *Engineering News,* Aug. 25, 1892, p. 187.
79 *Ibid.*
80 Act Number 204 of the Laws of Pennsylvania 1853.
81 *Ibid.,* Sec. 6.
82 Polytechnic College of Pennsylvania, *Pennsylvania School Journal,* July, 1853, p. 181.

By having wide geographical representation on the board of trustees and by not copying any one European school, Kennedy showed that he was interested in fashioning an American institution responsive to the needs of the state of Pennsylvania.

The development of the college and the fact that it was in existence as late as 1886 are shown in the following:

> . . . The institution began with two technical schools, those of Civil Engineering and of Chemistry and Metallurgy. In 1854 the School of Mechanical Engineering was added; in 1857 the School of Mines, and in 1858 the School of Architecture. The State aided the institution in 1867, by an appropriation of $5,000 but it has otherwise been compelled to rely for support wholly upon tuition fees and private subscription. When most prosperous it maintained a competent professor at the head of each of its departments, and was attended by a considerable body of students; but devoted as its President has always been to its interests, he has found it impossible of late years to prevent a marked reduction in the size of its classes.[83]

In addition to the above schools, that were operated within the college, an academic department was created in 1854 whose purpose is described in the 1854-55, eighteen page second annual announcement of the school as follows:

> This Department, recently organized by the Board of trustees, will be open in the College Building, on Monday, September 4, 1854.
> Students whose deficient English and Mathematical Education disqualify them from joining the College Classes, will be received into this department at any time, and be rapidly prepared by special instruction to enter college.[84]

The Location and Courses Offered.—The college was formally opened in what was originally a passenger depot of the central railroad at the corner of Penn Square and Market in Philadelphia. In 1860 the original building was sold and the college moved into a larger plant consisting of a main building four stories high on Market Street and two wings 117 feet long and three stories high. There is no mention in the literature as to how the money for this new building was obtained.

The Polytechnic College of Pennsylvania was ahead of both Rensselaer and the Massachusetts Institute of Technology in offering a large variety of technical and engineering courses. The following lists the courses of this school for the various degrees as given in the catalogue of the tenth session (1862-63).

---

[83] James P. Wickensham, *History of Education in Pennsylvania* (Lancaster, Pa.: Inquirer Publishing Company, 1886) p. 432.

[84] *Second Annual Announcement of the Polytechnic College of Pennsylvania,* Pamphlet Volume No. 15, Pennsylvania State Library, Harrisburg, Penn., p. 16.

FOR THE DEGREE OF BACHELOR OF CIVIL ENGINEERING

First Year Course
Mathematics
General Chemistry
General Physics
General Mechanics
Field Practice (Commenced)
Drawing (Topographical)
Mineralogy

Second Year Course
Mathematics, Civil Engineering,
   and Practical
Geology
Applied Mechanics
Architecture
Industrial Physics
Drawing and Modeling

FOR THE DEGREE OF BACHELOR OF MECHANICAL ENGINEERING

First Year Course
Mathematics
General Chemistry
General Physics
General Mechanics
Drawing (Mechanical)
Mineralogy

Second Year Course
Mathematics
Geology
Construction of Machines
Metallurgy
Applied Mechanics
Industrial Physics
Drawing and Architecture

FOR THE DEGREE OF BACHELOR OF CHEMISTRY

First Year Course
General Chemistry
General Physics
Mineralogy
Geology
Laboratory Practice

Second Year Course
Industrial Chemistry
Analytical Chemistry (Practical)
Agricultural Chemistry
Industrial Physics
Metallurgy
Natural History (Plants)
Drawing or a Modern Language

FOR THE DEGREE OF BACHELOR OF MINE ENGINEERING

First Year Course
Mathematics
General Chemistry
General Physics
General Mechanics
Mineralogy
Drawing

Second Year Course
Mathematics
Geology and Mineral Analysis
Mine Engineering
Applied Mechanics
Metallurgy
Industrial Physics
Drawing

FOR THE DEGREE OF BACHELOR OF ARCHITECTURE

First Year Course
Mathematics
General Chemistry
General Physics
General Mechanics
Mineralogy
Drawing and Coloring

Second Year Course
Mathematics
Geology
Industrial Physics and Chemistry
Applied Mechanics
Principles of Architecure
Modeling in Clay and Plaster
Drawing, Coloring and Designing

An examination of the above curricula shows the similarity between the courses offered for all the degrees with approximately three-fourths of the work common to all programs. In comparison it indicates the European influence as contrasted to the curricula of Rensselaer, Massachusetts Institute of Technology, and the University of Illinois previously presented. This European reflection is that all courses are technical in nature as contrasted to the study of English, Foreign Language and History contained in the other courses of study. Those deemed deficient in English and elementary Mathematics were required to take a preliminary year before enrolling in one of the professional courses.

The Enrollment and Degrees.—As complete records are not available a continuous picture of the institution over the years of its existence is not possible. There is sufficient material to indicate its prominence and although the school is not mentioned in the current literature the figures available show that it made a substantial contribution during the time of its operation.

The catalogue of 1855-56 lists 34 students in the professional schools and 33 students in the academic department giving a total of 67 students. The catalogue of 1862-63 is the most interesting of all. This picture of the college during the civil war lists 97 students and the granting of thirteen bachelor degrees and one master's degree. There were 7 "Bachelor of Civil Engineering," three "Bachelor of Mechanical Engineering" and two "Bachelor of Mine Engineering," and one "Bachelor of Chemistry." The degree of Master of Civil Engineering was awarded on the basis of three successful years of practice after receiving the degree of Bachelor of Civil Engineering. In granting thirteen bachelor degrees it granted the largest number of engineering degrees given by any institution in 1863. The corresponding figures for the other schools are Rensselaer (12), Harvard (5), Michigan (5), Yale (4), Dartmouth (2) and Union College (2).[85]

Other material on enrollments is limited to a listing in the Annual Report of the United States Commission of Education for the year 1877.[86] In this report the college is listed as having eleven full time staff and one part time professor. Sixty-five students were registered as taking the full course and four as taking a partial course. The course for this year is listed as being three years in length with the third year or senior class numbering twenty-one students. If all this class received degrees it would have been the second largest school with respect to graduating engineers, second to Rensselaer that graduated twenty-seven and ahead of Michigan that graduated eighteen. Another index of the school's importance is the number of engineering graduates that were members of the American Society of Civil Engineers during the

85 A. M. Wellington, *op. cit.*, p. 111.
86 Report of the U. S. Commissioner of Education, 1877, p. 541.

years between 1867 to 1892 as compiled by Wellington.[87] In this list the Polytechnic College of Pennsylvania is accredited with 19 graduates which places it eight in a list of forty-three schools. As a measure of relative importance these figures would be conservative as the school from its beginning was strong in divisions other than civil and many of its graduates may have joined the American Institute of Mining and Metallurgical Engineering founded in 1871 or the American Society of Mechanical Engineers founded in 1880.

There seems to be no explanation as to just why and when this school ceased to exist but from the material available it would appear that it operated up to 1886. Although generally forgotten it must be credited with offering regular curricula for the first time in mining engineering, mechanical engineering, and architecture which in itself gives it a place of distinction among early engineering schools.

[87] A. M. Wellington, *op. cit.,* Nov. 7, 1892, p. 471.

chapter 5

The Period of Rapid Growth in American Engineering Education (1863-1876)

Developments of the Period

The time interval between 1862 and 1875 included the civil war, the reconstruction period, the depression that began in 1873, and the Philadelphia Exposition of 1876. While an intense industrial expansion was ended by the year 1873, new engineering schools continued to be established throughout the complete period. The increase in engineering schools from seven in 1862 to seventy in 1872 and to eighty-five by 1880[1] was due in large part to the states' availing themselves of the opportunities afforded by the "Land Grant" or "Morill Act" of 1862. In addition to this unparalleled increase in numbers, many of these institutions developed new educational programs. Courses other than civil engineering began to be offered: shop instruction as an integral part of a program was introduced at Worcester Polytechnic Institute;[2] and the laboratory method as applied to engineering was started at Stevens Institute of Technology.[3]

The development of engineering education during this period still continued to be an almost exclusively academic educational movement, with the newly organized professional societies exerting their first influence. These societies initiated discussions questioning the effectiveness of the educational programs for producing practicing engineers. They also investigated the number of engineers being trained in relation to the number needed to satisfy the needs of the American economy. An understanding of this expanding economy, which showed its progressive advancement at the London Exposition of 1851, the Paris Exposition of 1867 and the Philadelphia Exposition of 1876, explains some of the pressures causing the establishment of the new engineering schools. This force did not act alone and must be evaluated in conjunction

[1] Charles R. Mann, *op. cit.*, p. 6.
[2] *Ibid.*, p. 75.
[3] R. H. Thurston, "Technical Education in the United States," *Transactions of the American Society of Mechanical Engineering*, 1893, Vol. 14, p. 938.

with the Morrill Act, the development of the engineering and other professions, and the educational system of which engineering was but one part. It is within this framework that a consideration of this period of rapid growth in engineering education is undertaken.

Industrial and Economic Conditions.—To state that from 1860 to 1880 the population increased from thirty-one million to forty million, while the percentage of urban population increased from 18.7 percent to 28.3 percent, would not give a true picture of the period. What happened was that the first economic effects of the Civil War threw the North and West into a severe panic.[4] This depression of 1861 gave way in the following spring to a revival of prosperity in the North and West.[5] This period of prosperity and expansion in the North and West, continued until 1873, when a severe depression set in that lasted up to 1879.[6] These alternating conditions of economic prosperity and depression had their effect on engineering education.

The depression of 1861 was short-lived because, while many men deserted the farms for the army and for the mines of the far West, this loss was offset by the work of women, an influx of immigrants from Europe, and by the use of labor saving machinery. The immigrants were attracted by railroad construction work and by the Homestead Act of 1862, which granted 160 acres of land to those who would live on their land five years. The production of new machinery during the civil war is described by Faulkner:

> Philadelphia, the largest center in the country, boasted 58 factories in 1862, 57 in 1863 and 65 in 1864, and other large cities showed similar progress. The war apparently contributed to the development of the nation's inventive genius, for the number of patents issued yearly more than doubled between 1860 and 1866.[7]

Manufacturing, stimulated by war needs and liberally protected by tariffs, accounted for the country's manufacturing products increasing during the decade between 1860 and 1870 about 52 percent or approximately twice as fast as the population.[8] The leading industries during this period were flour milling, slaughtering and meat packing, iron and steel, petroleum products, foundry and machine shop products, textiles, boots and shoes, ready-made clothing, farm implements, furniture, and distilled liquors.[9] While those products were being produced, the mines of the West were being worked, the first trans-Atlantic cable was laid and the railroad mileage was doubled. In addi-

---

[4] Emerson D. Fite, *Social and Industrial Conditions in the North During the Civil War,* 1910, p. 105.
[5] Harold Faulkner, *Economic History of the United States,* (New York: Harper Bros, 1949) p. 341.
[6] Victor S. Clark, *History of Manufacturing in the United States,* Vol. 2, p. 159.
[7] Harold Faulkner, *op. cit.,* p. 344.
[8] Victor S. Clark, *op. cit.,* p. 153.
[9] Reginald C. McGrane, *The Economic Development of the American Nation* (New York: Ginn and Company, 1942) p. 322.

tion to the above accomplishments the first trans-continental railroad was completed when the Union Pacific joined the Central Pacific in 1869.

The above facts suggest changes in the economy of America that provided the pressure for the establishment of mining engineering and mechanical engineering courses to supplement the single-stem civil engineering curriculum. It would also suggest that the prosperous time up to 1873 would produce private benefactions to establish engineering schools to stimulate further the industrial system that had proved so successful.

The increase in the number of schools graduating mining and mechanical engineers after 1862 could well have resulted from the conditions cited. Of the 1,305 engineers graduating in the decade following 1866, 79 percent were civil, 11 percent were mechanical and 10 percent were mining engineers.[10] With respect to private contributions, at least $5,000,000 is recorded as having been given to higher education in the '60's.[11] In addition, a list of private scientific schools compiled in 1889 reveals 26 founded between 1862 and 1888, of which 13 were established before 1874 and the remaining 13 after the depression in the years 1881 to 1888.[12] The fact that 13 schools were established between 1862 and 1874, as compared with seven in the fifty years prior to the Civil War is a measure of the willingness of capital to support technical education. The figures show that when the depression years were over, capital again contributed to founding new technical schools at a rate of approximately two a year between 1881 and 1888.

All of the above considerations apply to Northern and Western States. Without going into an extended treatment of the effect of the Civil War on industry and education in the Southern States, the following two quotations are given to summarize the situation and justify the limitations that have been placed on the previous discussion:

> The paralysis of all industrial operations due to the changed labor conditions, and the demoralization of all civil and judicial functions during the "carpet bag" regime, delayed the acceptance of the Government land grant for the establishment of colleges of agriculture and mechanic arts, in nearly all the Southern States. And even after it had been accepted, the early progress of the institutions was retarded by prejudice. To the old time Southerner, education meant literature and classics and did not mean anything else.[13]

This same thought is expressed by Drane in the following:

---

[10] Robert Fletcher, "The Present Status and Tendencies of Engineering Education in the United States," *Society for the Promotion of Engineering Education,* 1900, Vol. 8, p. 181.
[11] Harold Falkner, *op. cit.,* p. 349.
[12] *Report of the Commissioner of Education* 1880-1889, Government Printing Office, 1891, 1150-1157.
[13] John J. Wilmore, "Engineering Education in the South," *Society for the Promotion of Engineering Education,* 1898, Vol. 6, p. 58.

. . . the necessity for a new type of education arose, for the educational system of the old regime could not supply the needs of this rapid industrial growth . . . This preference for the classical education has a stronger hold in the south than in the north, and southern educators have been slower to accord engineering a place of dignity in their university curricula.[14]

Condition Up to 1862. — The educational concept of having land-grant colleges was an idea that developed over a period of approximately seventy-five years. The ordinance passed in 1787 for the sale of 1,500,000 acres of land to the "Ohio Company" made the first grant of two townships for a university. Under this original ordinance all states have received two townships (72 sections—46,000 acres) and a few have received a larger amount for the establishment of a state university.[15] Up to the time the first Morrill Land Grant Act was introduced into Congress in 1857, the federal government had already granted four million acres to fifteen states for the endowment of state universities.[16]

Except for the work of a few outstanding college presidents such as Nott of Union College, Folwell of Minnesota, Tappan of Michigan and Wayland of Brown, the colleges and universities of the Civil War period were of the classical type. Wayland, in his crusade for adapting the college courses to the different capacities and wants of the students, expressed in the following how the colleges were not preparing the students for the times in which they lived.

We have now in the United States . . . one hundred and twenty colleges pursuing in general this course. All of them teach Greek and Latin, but where are our classical scholars? All teach mathematics, but where are our mathematicians? We might ask the same questions concerning the other sciences taught among us. There has existed for the last twenty years a great demand for civil engineers. Has this demand been supplied from our colleges? We presume the single academy at West Point, graduating annually a smaller number than many of our colleges, has done more towards the construction of railroads than all our one hundred and twenty colleges united.[17]

Owing to the failure of Wayland and his group to change the educational practices of their time, the state universities were not adapted to training students in agriculture and the mechanic arts. This was recognized in 1850 by Massachusetts in an attempt to establish an agricultural college,[18] by Michigan in the same year with its congressional petition for 350,000 acres of land to

---

14 Walter H. Drane, "Engineering Education in Southern State Universities," *Society for the Promotion of Engineering Education,* 1903, Vol. 11, p. 225.
15 Paul Monroe (ed.) *A Cyclopedia of Education* (New York: Macmillan, 1925) p. 379.
16 Carl Becker, *Cornell University: Founders and Founding* (Ithaca, New York: Cornell University Press, 1943) p. 25.
17 Walter C. Bronsen, *op. cit.,* p. 261.
18 Charles A. Bennett, *History of Manual and Industrial Education Up to 1870* (Peoria, Ill.: Manual Arts Press, 1926) p. 354.

endow an agricultural college,[19] and by Illinois in 1852 with a memorial reading in part as follows:

> . . . And if possible on a sufficiently extensive scale to honorably justify a successful appeal to Congress, in conjunction with eminent citizens and statesmen in other States, who have expressed their readiness to cooperate with us, for an appropriate endowment of universities for the liberal education of the industrial classes in their several pursuits in each State of the Union.[20]

The urgency and foresight of these many attempts to change the collegiate system of the 1850,s were justified, as an excerpt from a report written by President Barnard of Columbia University in 1870 clearly indicates:

> In the twelve years before 1838 the rates of students to total population had grown, and in 1838 one in every 1,294 boys had gone to college. Thereafter the colleges had lost ground year by year until 1869, when the rate was one in every 1,927. Even in New England, the stronghold of education, where populaion had grown about 15% in 14 years, college enrollment had increased by only 3.3 percent.

The Morrill Act.—In 1857 Senator Justin S. Morrill of Vermont sponsored a bill for each state to receive 20,000 acres of public land for each representative and senator entitled to be in Congress by the census of 1850. The proceeds from this land were to be used for endowing colleges of agriculture and mechanics arts in the respective states.[22] This bill passed the house but failed in the Senate. Upon being resubmitted in 1859 it passed both the house and the senate, with twenty-five senators voting for it and twenty-two against it. The twenty-two dissenting votes included eighteen senators from the slave-holding states.[23] President Buchanan vetoed the bill and a new start had to be made.

In 1862 Senator Morrill sponsored a new bill that was similar to the first except that the land grant was increased to 30,000 acres, and instruction in military science and tactics was to be required for the established colleges. This bill was passed by both the house and the senate and was made into law by the signature of President Lincoln on July 2, 1862. The states were given until 1869 to accept the grant and until 1874 to open their schools. States yet to be admitted into the Union and states previously in rebellion were allowed to benefit from the Act.

Since its passage the act of 1862 has been changed in only two respects. In 1887 it was supplemented by the Hatch Act, which provided special sup-

---

[19] Paul Monroe (ed.) *op. cit.,* p. 380.

[20] Edmund J. James, *The Origin of the Land Grant Act of 1862: The University Studies* (Illinois: University of Illinois, 1910) p. 22.

[21] R. Hofstadter and C. D. Hardy, *The Development and Scope of Higher Education in the United States* (New York: Columbia University, 1952) p. 29.

[22] I. L. Kandel, *op. cit.,* p. 3.

[23] *Ibid.,* p. 13.

port for agricultural experiment stations. The second change, by the Act of 1890, overcame the disadvantage to which the small states were placed by the original act. Under this change each state regardless of size received $15,000 in 1890, with this cash grant increasing $1,000 a year for ten years. In this way each state has received $25,000 a year, for the purpose of the original act, since 1900.

It might well be assumed that with these federal land and money grants, the government would require a very definite type of state institution. It could also be assumed that the newly created colleges would be federally supervised to assure that formal requirements were being complied with. Both of these assumptions would be without foundation. Actually the wording of the act was very general, "if not vague," concerning the type of institution to be founded. The exact wording to this point is as follows:

> The proceeds were for "the endowment, support, and maintenance of at least one college where the leading object shall be, without excluding other scientific and classical studies, and including military tactics, to teach such branches of learning as are related to agriculture and the mechanic arts, in such manner as the legislature of the states may respectively prescribe, in order to promote the liberal and practical education of the industrial classes in the several pursuits and professions of life.[24]

From the above, the kind of school desired is not precisely clear. What is unmistakably clear, however, is that each state had the power, through its legislature, to determine what type of institution it should create to satisfy its own particular needs. The individual state institutions received no federal supervision of any kind. The only requirement of the law was that each college should submit an annual report for the following purpose:

> . . . recording any improvements and experiments made, with their costs and results, and such matter as may be supposed useful, to the other similarly endowed colleges, the Smithsonian Institution, and the agricultural division of the Patent Office.[25]

Mechanic Arts and Engineering.—During the first thirty years following passage of the Morrill Act there was considerable discussion concerning the term "Mechanic Arts" included in its title. To some this term was taken as applying to agriculture; to others it meant engineering, while another group gave it the broad title of trade education. Since the interpretation given determined the type of instruction offered, it is important to consider the basis of the various meanings given to the term, together with the interpretation supplied by Mr. Morrill.

---

[24] William S. Aldrich,"Engineering Education and the State University," *Society for the Promotion of Engineering Education,* Vol. 2 ,1894, p. 273.
[25] *Ibid.,* p. 274.

It has been stated that the term "Mechanic Arts," as used when the land grant act was being considered by Congress, was commonly employed synonymously with the terms "useful arts" and "industrial arts."[26] The dictionaries in common use at that time substantiate this point of view. In 1862 Webster's dictionary, under the word "art," states that the moderns divide the arts into the fine arts and the useful or mechanical arts; those arts in which the hands are more concerned than the mind are called "trades." Webster's dictionaries of 1855, 1860 and 1866 refer, under "art," to the fine arts and useful or mechanic arts.

In contrast to these rather broad definitions of "Mechanic Arts," Webster's dictionary of 1855 defines an engineer as one who constructs or manages engines or cannons, while his 1860 edition refers to : (1) Military engineers; (2) maker of engines; (3) one who manages a steam engine; (4) a civil engineer, as one who constructs canals, docks, railroads, etc. The Encyclopia Britannica dated 1857 states that mechanics, applicable or applied, is a term which, strictly speaking, includes all applications of the principles of abstract mechanics to human acts. Thus it is seen that the term "Mechanic Arts" was broader than engineering, and the fact that the word "trade" was not employed would imply that the instruction should be based on the mental rather than the manual aspect of the mechanic of useful arts.

To help clear up the many misunderstandings concerning the instructional intent of the act, Mr. Morrill was invited in 1867 to confer with the faculty of the Sheffield Scientific School on his interpretation of the law. Professor Brewer, a member of the faculty, took notes on the conference, at which Mr. Morrill stated that the new schools should be of college grade, utilizing science rather than the classics as their leading feature.[27] He further stated that there were sufficient classical colleges in existence, while there was a need for more colleges to teach the useful sciences and adapt them to the conditions and necessities of the several states. The word "engineering" is not reported as having been used at this meeting. At a later date, on December 23, 1890, Senator Morrill in a letter to E. W. Stanton of Ames, Iowa, made the following statement: "Civil engineering in the agricultural college is perhaps one of the most useful branches of the mechanic arts that can be taught and, of course, it was included in the act of 1862."[28] The final definition was formulated some fifty years after the passage of the act. This was done in the following words of the executive committee of the Association of Land Grant Colleges on November 13, 1914.

Mechanic Arts is a broad educational term, which includes engineering

---

[26] "Survey of Land-Grant Colleges and Universities," U. S. *Department of the Interior,* Vol. 1, 1930, p. 797.
[27] *Ibid.,* p. 9.
[28] *Ibid.,* p. 797.

education as its higher or professional phase, trade-school and short-course instruction as its collateral and extensive phase, and experimental and other technical investigations as its research phase.[29]

Although this official definition by the colleges took fifty years to evolve, the land-grant institutions from their beginning understood "Mechanic Arts" to include engineering, as the following discussion will emphasize:

Colleges Established Under the Morrill Act.—Owing to the Civil War, considerable delay occurred in establishing institutions under the new act. Aside from Kansas, which took action in 1863, and Vermont, in 1866, the states waited until the war was over before embarking on this new educational venture. In creating the new schools the states exercised their right to establish the type of institution that best suited their needs. Massachusetts divided the fund in such way that Massachusetts Agricultural College received two-thirds. Four states used the grant to endow departments and schools already existing in private institutions within their states. Schools so benefiting were Sheffield Scientific School in Connecticut, Brown University in Rhode Island, Rutgers in New Jersey, and Cornell in New York State. Eighteen states added the endowments to that of their state universities and combined the two institutions into one. Some examples of this practice were in Wisconsin, Minnesota, Missouri, Illinois, Vermont, Maine and New Hampshire. Virginia and Alabama founded specialized polytechnic institutions. The remaining states established separate schools known variously as Colleges of Agriculture and Mechanic Arts, Agricultural and Mechanical Colleges, Agricultural Colleges, or simply State Colleges.[30]

These many institutions operating under a variety of names and controls were all charged with the responsibility of teaching agriculture and the mechanic arts. Since the Morrill Act received strong support from farm groups, an early attempt was made to develop programs for the farmers. The statement of aims in the early catalogues would give the impression that the colleges existed for giving a trade-school type of training for the farmers. For example, the 1868-69 catalogue of the University of Wisconsin stated:

> It is the design of the University to give in this department a thorough course of instruction directly pertaining to agriculture which will enable our graduates to conduct the operation of a farm both intelligently and profitably.[31]

As early as 1867 Barnard criticized those who seemed to make agricultural training the only purpose of the "Land Grant Colleges."

[29] *Ibid.*, p. 798.
[30] Charles S. Murkland, "The Agricultural College," *Society for the Promotion of Engineering Education*, Vol. 5, 1898, p. 305.
[31] Frederick S. Mumford, *The Land Grant College Movement* (Columbia, Missouri: Experiment Station Bulletin, No. 419, 1880) p. 29.

The act is almost always called the "Agricultural College Bill," which is as truly a misnomer as if it were called the "Public Lands Bill . . . ." The mechanic arts, however, are placed on the same footing as agriculture, and the liberal education of the industrial classes in as much an object of the grant as their practical training. In short, any branch of human learning may lawfully receive attention in these schools, provided only that it does not preclude attention to the study of natural science in the application to human industry.[32]

In spite of the attempt to emphasize the agricultural program in the colleges, there was little demand for the agricultural courses. This lack of interest has been attributed to a variety of causes. It has been stated that since the movement was not a grass roots affair the farmer himself was not sympathetic.[33] In addition, as has been demonstrated, there was considerable confusion as to just what type of course should be taught.[34] There was also difficulty in obtaining qualified faculty that could teach applied agriculture. A description of this teaching situation is given by Hofstadter and Hardy:

> On the right they were menaced by an infiltration of old-style educators who had no understanding of and little sympathy for the needs of a diversified science faculty. Thus Texas A and M had a chair of chemistry, natural science and agriculture, taught by a doctor of divinity; the Kansas Agricultural College inherited its faculty from a denominational school, and with it a ministerial president; one college added horticultural instruction to the teaching duties of the professor of languages; and the Florida State College of Agriculture had a professorship of agricul, ture, horticulture, and Greek.[35]

The discussion as to whether agricultural courses should be trade and farm courses or scientific and professional continued for some years. Had the wording "mechanic arts" been literally interpreted according to its previous usage, the result could have been school shops, trade teaching or a substitute apprenticeship plan.[36] The combined effects of industrial pressure and the successes of the established engineering schools resulted in the term "mechanic arts" being interpreted to mean engineering. In this regard Mumford states that from the beginning the engineering programs of the land-grant colleges were more successful than the agricultural programs.[37] This success would have to be interpreted in terms of the type of program rather than of the number of graduates. This is because the land-grant colleges up to the

[32] Henry Barnard, "Our National Schools of Science," North American Review (Vol. 105, July-Oct., 1867) p. 507.
[33] Charles A. Bennett, op. cit., p. 354.
[34] Edward D. Eddy, Colleges of Our Land and Time (New York: Harper & Brothers, 1956) p. 51.
[35] R. Hofstadter and C. D. Hardy, op. cit., p. 40.
[36] Carter and Scot (ed.) Dictionary of Education (New York: McGraw-Hill Book Company, 1945) p. 32.
[37] Frederick B. Mumford, op. cit., p. 77.

year 1872-73, had graduated a total of 1,391, of whom 427 were in agriculture, 243 in engineering and 591 in science and the classics.[38] A further discussion of these figures, together with other statistics concerning engineering education will be of interest.

For the period from 1862 to 1876 inclusive, a national total of 1,866 engineers were graduated.[39] Of this number, 795 were from the few private schools founded prior to the civil war, while the remaining 1,071 were from universities not included in the land grant act of 1862. This means that of the total of 1,866 graduates for the period, only 243 were engineering graduates of land-grant colleges. These figures indicate that the land-grant college was in a period of development and its main contribution during this time was in the philosophy it established and the number of institutions founded. Of more interest than the number of graduates produced by these new state colleges is the direction they gave to American higher education in general and to engineering education in particular. This could well account for the belief that credits the new colleges with extending the opportunities for engineering education rather than influencing the institutional type of curriculum under which it was to operate.

The Morrill Land-Grant Act of 1862 stimulated the rapid extension of engineering, but did little to determine its distinctive form and character. The development of land-grant institutions made this type of education widely accessible to the industrial classes, and many of the most notable engineering colleges of the United States were established directly or indirectly as a result of the Morrill Act.[40]

Of special interest in this connection was the idea that the state had an obligation to support a form of higher education designed to meet the needs of a growing industrial economy. This it accomplished by making an engineering training available to the industrial and agricultural classes whose academic preparation was limited to the public school education available at the time. In establishing these engineering schools within the framework of a college, the concept of professional training for engineering as an integral part of a four year college program became more deeply rooted. This strengthening of the college engineering school has provided little chance for engineering to develop strictly professional schools similar to the law and medical schools. A third consideration revealed by the number of degrees granted by the land-grant colleges for the year 1872-73 is of interest. These figures indicate that at the time the state land-grant schools were well on their way to being state colleges in the modern sense of the word. When 591 of the 1,391 graduates were in science and the classics, it indicates that many were selecting the state schools in preference to the classical colleges for their general studies.

38 L. L. Kandel, op. cit., p. 99.
39 A. M. Wellington, op. cit., Table XVI, p. 139.
40 Survey of Land-Grant Colleges and Universities, op. cit., p. 790.

Special Instructional Features of Schools Founded During This Period

The administration form of the engineering schools founded between 1862 and 1875 followed patterns set by the relatively new schools founded prior to the civil war. For both private and state-supported institutions three distinct administrative structures evolved. Basically these three types were: (1) self-contained technological institutes such as Rensselaer, Massachusetts Institute of Technology, Stevens Institute, and Alabama Polytechnic Institute; (2) separate schools of engineering or mining associated with a college or university, as at Columbia, Harvard, Yale, University of Michigan and Cornell; and (3) engineering departments within a college, as at Union, Brown, Maine and many of the first state colleges.

Under these common institutional types a number of special educational features developed that are of importance in evaluating the progress in engineering education during this period of rapid growth. Under this heading the contributions of Massachusetts Institute of Technology, Worcester Polytechnic Institute, Stevens Institute of Technology, Thayer School at Dartmouth, and Cornell University warrant special study.

Massachusetts Institute of Technology.—The Rogers plan of 1861 had envisioned a triple organization of the institute, consisting of a Society of Arts, a Museum, and a School of Industrial Science and Arts. This multiple-purpose institution was not established, as the following statement of aims printed in the first catalogue for the first regular session that opened Oct. 2, 1865, indicates:

> First, To provide a full course of scientific studies and practical exercises for students seeking to qualify themselves for the profession of the Mechanical Engineer, Civil Engineer, Practical Chemist, Engineer of Mining, and a Builder and Architect.
>
> Second, To furnish such a general education, founded upon the Mathematical, Physical and Natural Sciences, English and other Modern Languages and Mental and Political Science, as shall form a fitting preparation for any of the departments of active life; and—
>
> Third, To provide courses of Evening Instruction in the main branches of knowledge above referred to, for persons of either sex, who are prevented by occupation or other causes, from devoting themselves to scientific study during the day, but who desire to avail themselves of systematic evening lessons or lectures.

This same catalogue describes the various curricula in detail and lists the same courses for all students in the first two years, with specialized training reserved for the third and fourth years. This practice changed in 1873, with specialization starting with the second year.

M. I. T. is here mentioned because it was the first truly technological institute that continues to exist, and because of the constant effort to adjust its offerings to meet community needs. The Rensselaer Polytechnic Institute that dated back to 1823 was at this date chiefly a school of civil engineering and did not offer the variety of courses that Massachusetts Institute of Technology did. The latter's concept of meeting a community need extended beyond the offering of the several branches of engineering, mining and architecture. The course in General Science and Literature included in the first catalogues was designed to "furnish such a general education . . . as shall form a fitting preparation for any of the departments of active life."[41] This course indicated that from the beginning the institute was to offer more than specific professional training by providing an alternate road to a general education for those not suited to the typical liberal arts college. This idea was reinforced in 1871 when the seventh department, "Natural History," was established to prepare students for medicine, agriculture, geology, mineralogy and rural economy.[42] Outside of the degree programs of study, the institute participated in or sponsored other programs that were a part of its service to the community. Within the curriculum structure special students were allowed, as Prescott shows:

> In addition to the regular students, the school welcomed as special students young men who could attend only for a single year or even a single term, primarily to get instruction in some limited field in which interest, apptitude, or previous occupation had brought the ambition to increase their knowledge and prepare themselves for better positions.[43]

An evening school supported by the Lowell Foundation now known as the Lowell School of Design took the place of what the Institute planned as its evening courses. These courses continue to the present day and are held in the institute's buildings and are taught by the staff of the Institute. In addition, summer excursions were conducted for many students of geology, and civil and mechanical engineering. These became the forerunners of more highly developed summer schools.

When President Rogers returned from the Philadelphia Exposition of 1876 he was so impressed by the Russian Industrial Arts exhibits that he established a School of Mechanic Arts as part of the work of the Institute. Prescott describes the school:

> The School of Mechanic Arts, unlike the Lowell School of Design, was a specialized division of the Institute designed to train factory technicians and shop managers. Students pursuing their program were registered as specials.[44]

In the building constructed for this school a women's laboratory was established in 1876 through the support of the Women's Educational Associa-

41 Massachusetts Institute of Technology Catalogue 1890-91, Cambridge, Mass., p. 42.
42 Samuel C. Prescott, op. cit., p. 93.
43 Ibid., p. 52.
44 Ibid., p. 98.

tion of Boston. Its purpose was to afford instruction in chemical analysis, industrial chemistry, mineralogy and natural history. This school was discontinued in 1883, six years before the School of Mechanic Arts was closed.

The success of the Massachusetts Institute of Technology was almost immediate; the 74 students registered in 1865 increased to 384 by 1872. The first three graduating classes, 1868 to 1870, received diplomas, but from 1871 on the bachelor of science degree was conferred. The school was designed after Rogers' plan, and emphasized the idea that the proper place for engineering training was a four-year undergraduate course with technical cultural subjects combined to provide a broad education. The plan also assumed that within the program of a technological institute a sound scientifically orientated cultural education was possible. It is of interest that this school, with its 384 enrollment and 34 faculty members in 1872[45] was doing what the Lawrence gift charged the Lawrence Scientific School to do at Harvard, only three miles away. At this same time the Lawrence Scientific School had only Professor Eustis and Mr. Dean teaching engineering, and graduated only three students in 1871, one in 1872 and eleven in 1873, with its maximum enrollment having been 79 in 1865, the year the Massachusetts Institute of Technology started its classes.[46] This disparity between the accomplishments of the two schools prompted an attempt by Harvard to form an alliance between the schools: the one poor in resources but thriving educationally, the other comparatively rich but without the ability to attract sufficient students to justify its program. This first unsuccessful attempt was to be followed by several more during the Institute's first fifty years.

Worcester Polytechnic Institute.—In 1865, John Boynton, a successful merchant with limited formal education, entrusted his cousin, David Whitcomb, with the sum of $100,000 for the endowment of a free school. This school was to be located in Worcester, Massachusetts, if the citizens would provide the land and suitable buildings. The latter condition was complied with by a gift of land and $61,111 contributed by 232 individuals and by twenty shops and factories.[47] In the same year Ichabod Washburn, a Worcescester manufacturer, gave an initial $25,000 anl later an additional $50,000, to establish a machine shop as a department of the new school. Washburn's interest was to have established what would now be understood as a trade school with instruction in the principles of science added.

On March 20, 1868, Charles O. Thompson, a Dartmouth graduate, was elected principal, with the opening of school being postponed until November 1st in order that Thompson might visit the technical schools of Europe.

[45] *Ibid.,* p. 50.

[46] A. M. Wellington, "The Lawrence Scientific School," *Engineering News* (May 19, 1892) p. 515.

[47] Charles G. Washburn, "Technical Education in Relation to Industrial Development," *Journal of the Worcester Polytechnic Institute,* Vol. 9, 1906, p. 339.

Thompson found little in the previously organized American schools that could be adapted to his rather novel aim of combining theoretical and manual work. Most helpful in developing the Worcester plan were the ideas gathered from the technical schools of France and Germany, and especially those from the Imperial School of Moscow.[48] The concepts developed and enunciated by Thompson at the opening of the school in 1858 are given by Clarke:

1. That all mechanical engineers will find their credit, in the future, in going through a workshop training.
2. This workshop instruction is best given in a genuine manufacturing machine shop where work is done that is to be sold in open market, and in unprotected competition with the products of other shops.
3. The workshop instruction may precede, accompany or follow the intellectural training, but for many reasons it preferably accompanies it.
4. That in a course of 3½ years, working 800 hours the first half year and 500 hours a year thereafter, a boy beginning without any knowledge of mechanics may acquire skill enough to offer himself at graduation as a journey man, and will be found on trial not inferior to those who have spent the entire time of 3½ years in a regular machine shop.
5. That the workshop practice must be a part of every week's work in the instruction; that it shall be momentarily supervised by skillful men, and that the student must not expect to receive any pecuniary advantage from it.[49]

At the time of its opening a three year course was offered, which was increased to three and one-half years in 1875 and finally to four years in 1893. The first five months of the first year were spent in the shop in what was called a preparatory or apprentice class. The upper classes spent ten hours a week in the shops in addition to the month of July. Students taking civil engineering spent an equivalent amount of time in field work.

It would be expected that this combination apprentice and technical course would draw its students almost exclusively from the laboring and industrial class. Actually one-half the first class were the sons of artisans, mechanics, and farmers. The other half were the sons of clergymen, manufacturers, and a doctor. At the first commencement 15 students graduated with diplomas. Diplomas were given to the first four classes, with the agreement that graduates would receive bachelor of science degrees when they proved they had applied themselves both honorably and successfully to their profession for a period of four years. On a petition from the alumni the trustees changed this practice in 1875

[48] Herbert J. Taylor, *Seventy Years of the Worcester Polytechnic Institute* (Worcester, Mass.: Davis Press, 1935) p. 18.
[49] Isaac E. Clarke, "Industrial and Technical Training in Schools of Technology and in United States Land-Grant Colleges," *U.S. Bureau of Education* 1898, p. 726.

so that all graduates after this date recived their degrees upon completion of their course.[50]

The school's name was originally the Worcester County Free Institute of Industrial Science, which was later changed to the Worcester Technical Institute; since 1889 it has been the Worcester Polytechnic Institute. The work of its students was displayed at the Philadelphia Exhibition of 1876, with the result that the newly organized Rose Polytechnic Institute copied its type of instruction and eventually in 1882 installed Thompson from Worcester as its president. With the loss of Thompson and changing industrial conditions, Worcester Polytechnic, which was designed to train mechanical superintendents, became after twenty years a general college of engineering.[51]

Thayer School of Civil Engineering.—The school was established in 18-67 by a gift from Sylvanus Thayer, who has been mentioned as the "Father of West Point." Thayer School has the distinction of being the first engineering school founded by an engineer and of being form its beginning a graduate school of civil engineering. Thayer, when making his gift, stipulated exactly the requirements for admission, the curriculum, and the first director of the school he desired to found.

The requirement for admission was very high for the times and included besides the subjects taught in the common schools, algebra, geometry, mensuration, trigonometry, compass surveying, descriptive geometry, geometrical drawing, analytical geometry, differential and integral calculus, elementary mechanics, a full course of elemntary physics, elements of inorganic chemistry, meteorology, and physical astronomy.[52] The school was designed to be essentially post-graduate in nature with a course of at least two years duration, which might be lengthened to three years. In 1870 General Thayer appointed Robert Fletcher, a 1865 graduate of West Point, as director of the school. Fletcher, who took up his duties in 1871, retained the position of director for forty-seven years, up to the year 1918.

Due to the entrance requirements and the limitations of the curriculum to civil engineering alone, the number of students did not average more than five a year up to 1876.[53] The curriculum that gradually evolved consisted of three years at Dartmouth College and two years in the Thayer School. After the first year in the Thayer School, a Bachelor of Arts degree was conferred, counting the first year of professional studies as the fourth year of college. At the end of the second year at Thayer School the professional degree of "civil engineer" was granted. This program was not followed by other institu-

[50] Herbert Taylor, *op. cit.,* p. 72.
[51] "Report of the Committee Investigating Engineering Education 1923-29," *Society for the Promotion of Engineering Education,* p. 820.
[52] A. M. Wellington, "Thayer School of Dartmouth," *Engineering News* (May 26, 1892) p. 542.
[53] *Ibid.,* p. 543.

tions, but is of interest because it did offer a method, at on early date, of separating the general education studies from the professional courses and putting engineering education on a basis similar to that developed by the medical and legal professions.

Cornell University.—This institution deserves mention as one of the most influential early land-grant colleges. Though essentially an independent institution, it received the land grants of the state of New York and operated under the dual capacity of private and state school. Its liberal policy was expressed by Ezra Cornell in the statement: "I would found an institution where any person can find instruction in any study."[54] Operating under this policy the university encouraged the older and newer educational disciplines to develop on even terms.

Cornell opened for instruction in 1868, with the founder advising that the school of mechanic arts be a manual labor college using the water power on the campus to operate manufacturing plants that would employ student labor.[55] The president, Andrew D. White, asserted that the need for trained artisans could be satisfied by the public and trade schols, while the duty of Cornell was to furnish "captains in the army of industry."[56] In settling this question White did much to clarify for many colleges of the time the intent of the Morrill Act. In his own words he stated: ". . . that our main purpose must be to send out into all parts of the State and Nation thoroughly trained graduates, who should develop and improve the main industries of the country, and by their knowledge and example, train up skillful artisans of various sorts in every locality."[57]

To accomplish this well-designed purpose White organized his engineering college into a school of civil engineering, a school of mechanical engineering, and a school of architecture. The directors of these schools were independent of each other and responsible only to the president. These schools had a rapid growth, graduating 75 civil engineers, 15 mechanical engineers and 17 architects up to and including the year 1876.[58] The degrees granted at the end of the four year course were CE and ME rather than the BS degree. For the year 1875 there were 82 civil and 56 mechanical engineering students enrolled. These numbers were not large compared to the 404 degrees conferred by the University during the period. Compared to the six degrees granted in agriculture, the numbers were large and indicate the popularity of the Mechanic Arts as compared to agriculture courses. This popularity was a real issue at

[54] A. M. Wellington, "Cornell University," *Engineering News* (July 28, 1892) p. 783.
[55] Report of Investigation of Engineering Education, *op. cit.,* p. 818.
[56] Walter P. Rogers, *Andrew White and the Modern University* (Ithaca, New York Cornell University Press, 1942) p. 112.
[57] *Autobiography of Andrew D. White* (Ithaca, New York: Cornell University Press, 1939) p. 155.
[58] M. E. Wardsworth, "Some Statistics in Engineering Education," *Transactions of American Institute of Mining Engineering,* Vol. 27, 1897, p. 729.

the time, and was of such concern to White that he required "that no person shall receive a degree in any regular course in the University without having had a course and passed the examination there upon in general agriculture."[59] This required course failed to stimulate enthusiasm, as did the free tuition offered to agricultural students in 1873.

Though the agricultural and mechanic arts divisions of the University received the New York state land grants as an initial endowment, the state beyond this did practically nothing to support the institution. It was supported by a large number of gifts from many sources that enabled the school to expand as the need arose. While the expansion was taking place, it could well have influenced Rensselaer to abolish its newly created departments of mechanical and mining engineering in 1871.[60] This allowed Rensselaer to concentrate on civil engineering, leaving mechanical engineering to Cornell and Stevens Institute, and mining to the Columbia School of Mines. Cornell, however, did not curtail the development of its school of civil engineering. Actually it expanded all of its schools to the extent of graduating more civil engineers per year than Rensselaer did by the year 1890.

Stevens Institute of Technology.—This institution was founded in 1871 from a bequest of Robert Stevens, who had been a member of a prominent engineering family. Though given the broad title of Stevens Institute of Technology, the school from its beginning conferred but a single degree, that of Mechanical Engineer.

Dr. Henry Morton, a graduate of the University of Pennsylvania with the class of 1857, was its first president from 1871 to 1902. He was a successful teacher and his lectures on science drew as many as 3,500 people with the same number for the repeat performance on the following evening.[61] Morton supplemented the professional courses with a general educational program described by him:

> A department of Belles-Letters will be included and will furnish the means of acquiring that culturation of literary taste and facility in the graceful use of language, both in speaking and writing, which is as desirable in the engineer and men of science as in the classical student.[62]

Stevens' enrollment was small, increasing from forty-one students in 1872 to ninety-seven in 1876.[63] It is mentioned not for the number of students it trained, but for the fact that it was founded to be a school of mechanical engineering only, and because under Thurston it developed in 1873 the first engineering laboratory in America. The laboratory referred to was an experi-

[59] Autobiography of Andrew D. White, *op. cit.,* p. 118.
[60] Palmer C. Ricketts, *op. cit.,* p. 112.
[61] R. H. Thurston, *op. cit.,* p. 338.
[62] A. M. Wellington, "Stevens Institute of Technology," *Engineering News* (July 21, 1892) p. 65.
[63] M. E. Worthington, *op. cit.,* p. 721.

mental method of instruction in mechanical engineering in contrast with the shop courses that were introduced into a number of curricula before this date.

Professional Societies

Preliminary Considerations.—In England the Institute of Civil Engineers was esablished in 1818 as an outgrowth of Smeaton's Club of 1771. This organization adopted Tredgold's famous definition of engineering, "The art of utilizing the forces of nature for the use and convenience of man."[64] The Institute, incorporated by a Royal Charter in 1828, grew steadily, and by 1867 had gained 1, 339 members.[65] American engineering education was firmly established before the profession became an organized body. The Boston Society of Civil Engineers was founded in 1848, the American Society of Civil Engineers in 1852, the American Institute of Mining Engineers in 1871, the American Society of Mechanical Engineering in 1880 and the American Institute of Electrical Engineers in 1884. Curricula for these branches of engineering were developed and taught before the practicing engineers organized their societies. In this respect engineering education developed almost independently of the profession, in contrast to the medical, dental and legal professions, whose societies were from the beginning intimately connected with the educational process.

An analysis of their respective purposes reveals the interest of the engineering societies in the education of engineers already practicing. The other professional societies were concerned with professional education preparatory to practice.To allustrate this point the objectives of these two types of organizations are given.

Institute of Civil Engineers.—The purpose of this organization is set forth in the following part of its Royal Charter of 1828:

> George the Fourth, by the Grace of God, of the United Kingdom of Great Britain and Ireland King, Defender of the Faith: to all of whom these presents shall come Greetings:
> Whereas Thomas Telford, of Abingdon Street, in our city of Westminster, Esquire, a Fellow of the Royal Societies of London and Edinburgh, and others of our loving subjects, have formed themselves into a Society for the general advancement of Mechanical Science, and more particularly for promoting the acquisition of that species of knowledge which constitutes the profession of a Civil Engineer, being the art of directing the great sources of power in nature for the use and convenience of man, as the means of production and of traffic in states both for external and internal trade, as applied in the construction of roads, bridges, aqueducts, canals, river navigation, and docks, for internal intercourse

---

[64] James K. Finch, *Engineering in Western Civilization* (New York: McGraw-Hill, 1951) p. 52.
[65] W. J. McAlpine, "President's Address of 1858," *Transactions of American Society of Civil Engineers*, Vol. 1, 1872, p. 46.

and exchange, and in the construction of ports, harbours, moles, break-waters, and lighthouses, and in the art of navigation by artificial power for the purposes of commerce, and in the construction and adaptation of machinery, and in the drainage of cities and towns . . .[66]

Boston Society of Civil Engineers.—This society was organized July 3, 1848 and incorporated April 25, 1851 for the purpose of:

The professional improvement of the members, the encouragement of social intercourse among engineers and men of practical science, and the advancement of engineering.[67]

American Society of Cicil Engineers.—This society was organized in New York City in 1852. Its activities were discontinued between 1855 and 1867 due to a lack of interest and members. The society was re-established in 1868. Its objectives are stated in the second article of its constitution and by the following statement from the "President's Address of 1870:"

. . . The professional development of its members; the encouragement of social intercourse among men of practical science; the advancement of engineering in its several branches, and the establishment of a central point of reference and union for its members.

Our society has been established for the purpose of advancing knowledge, science, and practical experience among its members, by an exchange of thoughts, studies and experiences.[68]

American Institute of Mining Engineers.—This society was established in 1871, with the following aims adopted in May, 1873:

The objects of the American Institute of Mining Engineers are to promote the Arts and Sciences connected with the economical production of the useful minerals and metals, and the welfare of those employed in these industries, by means of meeting for social intercourse, and the reading and discussion of professional papers, and to circulate, by means of publication among its members and associates, the information thus obtained.[69]

American Society of Mechanical Engineers.—The objects of this society, which was founded in 1880, were stated by its president:

The objects to be attained by this Society, if the wishes and expectations of its founders are carried out, are the promotion of "the arts and sciences connected with engineering and mechanical construction," by the establishment of regular meetings to be attended by members of the engineering profession.[70]

[66] T. J. Hoover and J. C. Fish, *The Engineering Profession* (Stanford, California: Stanford University Press, 1950) p. 19.
[67] "Scientific and Technical Societies of the United States and Canada," *Natural Research Council Publication No. 369*, p. 132.
[68] A. W. Cravens, "President's Address of 1870," *Transactions of American Society of Civil Engineers*, Vol. I, 1872, p. 219.
[69] *Transactions of the American Institute of Mining Engineers*, Vol. 12, 1884, p. XIV.
[70] R. H. Thurston, "The President's Address," *Transactions of the American Society of Mechanical Engineers*, Vol. 1, 1880, p. 4.

Holley, in the same *Transactions* of the Society, gives the following three objectives of the organization. Like all those quoted they make no mention of the education of prospective members of the profession:

1. The most obvious advantage is the collection and diffusion of definite and much needed information by means of papers and discussions.
2. A less obvious, but, it seems to me, a more important advantage of an organization is the general acquaintance thus promoted and by no other means promoted, among engineers and the businessmen associated with them.
3. The habit of writing and discussing technical papers is of great importance.[71]

American Medical Association.—This organization was founded in 1845 by co-ordinating the efforts of previously formed local organizations. In describing the movement, the purpose of the Association is stated by Flexner:

. . . eleven years later (1846) an agitation set up by Nathan Smith Davis resulted in the formation of the American Medical Association, committed to two propositions, viz., that it is desirable "that young men received as students of medicine should have acquired a suitable preliminary education," and "that a uniform elevated standard of requirements for the degree of M.D. should be adopted by all the medical schools in the United States."[72]

American Society of Dental Surgeons.—When the medical schools refused to teach dental surgery as a part of their course, the first school was founded in 1840 in Baltimore. The following description of this founding indicates the important part played by the Dental Society in professional education:

The American Society of Dental Surgeons, composed of the leading physician dentists and dentists in all parts of the country, reacted constructively to organized medicine's disapprobation of dentistry by giving to this first dental school (Baltimore College of Dental Surgery) the Society's unqualified approval and support.[73]

American Bar Association.—The many bar associations that were organized following the civil war were finally coordinated into the American Bar Association. In stating the problems involved in founding this new association, the place of education assumes major importance as the following indicates:

Three problems in particular have given trouble from the start—the relation, namely, between these new associations and the entire body of

71 *Ibid.,* p. 10.
72 Abraham Flexner, "Medical Education in the United States and Canada," Bulletin No. 4, *Carnegie Foundation for the Advancement of Teaching,* 1910, p. 10.
73 William J. Gils, "Dental Education in the United States and Canada," Bulletin No. 19, *Carnegie Foundation for the Advancement of Teaching,* 1926, p. 40.

lawyers—the relation between the local and national elements of the new composite organization—the relation, finally, between this practitioner's organization and the schools.[74]

Educational Influence of Societies. — The forces responsible for the founding of our engineering colleges did not include influences from the practicing professions within the period being considered. The stated purposes of the newly formed engineering societies did not include provisions for guiding or controlling professional education, as did the societies of law, medicine and dentistry. This condition could help explain why engineering education remained in the college while the other groups developed professional curricula distinct from the college.

The numbers that belonged to the engineering societies should be considered. In 1870 there were 179 members of the American Society of Civil Engineers, as compared to the 7,374 listed as engineers of that date.[75] Both these numbers are significant, since up to 1870 only 866 engineers had graduated in the United States. This means that only a maximum of twenty percent of these graduates could have been interested in joining the Society. The figures also indicate that approximately 88 percent of the 7,374 men who designated themselves as engineers must have received their training by apprentice methods. This could well explain why there was a lack of interest in formal engineering education among the engineers themselves, and why, during this first half century of its growth engineering education developed without guidance from the profession.

Engineering Curricula

General Curriculum Considerations.—This period of rapid growth of American engineering schools corresponded to one of arrested development in French technical education.[76] Though dependent upon foreign text-books, American engineering education turned away from European models, and developed a pattern of its own consistent with American influences.[77] These influences included a need for practical experiences within the curricula, courses in mining and mechanical engineering to meet industry's new demands, and the use of the basic American college curriculum that was the model of American higher education.

[74] Alfred Z. Reed, "Training for the Public Profession of the Law," Bulletin No. 15, *Carnegi Foundation for the Advancement of Teaching*, 1921, p. 204.

[75] *Report of the United States Bureau of Education*, (Washington, D.C.: U.S. Printing Office, 1870).

[76] William E. Wickenden, "A Comparative Study of Engineering Education in the United States and Canada," Bulletin No. 16, Investigation of Engineering Education, 1923-1929, *Society for the Promotion of Engineering Education*, 1930, p. 767.

[77] "A Study of Evolutionary Trends in Engineering Curricula," Bulletin No. 11, Investigation of Engineering Education, 1923-1929, *Society for the Promotion of Engineering Education*, p. 547.

Practical Courses.—Practice became part of the curriculum through the establishing of shop and surveying courses, laboratory instruction, and summer inspection trips. Shop work was a controversial issue, and the courses offered varied from a substitute for apprenticeship, as developed at Worcester, to the Russian system of teaching basic but elementary skills and procedures, as utilized at M. I. T. and Maine.[78] In the majority of cases a happy mean, as achieved at Cornell, was the rule. Though the controversy reflected a basic difference in aim and attitude, it was of little consequence, since shop work became of minor importance before the issue was settled.[79]

Mining and Mechanical Engineering.—The first mining and mechanical engineering degree courses were offered by the Polytechnic College of Pennsylvania, and were discontinued when the school ceased to operate. The earliest mining course still in existence was established at the Columbia School of Mines in 1863. During the period up to 1876 the mining engineering curriculum was a special adaptation of the basic civil engineering course that had previously developed. The schools offering mining were not specialized institutions but general engineering schools, as represented by the University of Michigan, M. I. T., Rensselaer, Yale, Washington and Lee, Lafayette, Lehigh, University of California, and Washington University, all of which awarded mining engineering degrees during this period.[80] Even the Columbia School of Mines with its specialized title developed into a generalized school of applied science, and from its core curriculum offered the additional degree of civil engineer in 1868.[81]

The first mechanical engineering course, still in existence, was instituted at Yale in 1863.[82] In 1870 this course was raised to a graduate level and named dynamical engineering. This name was selected by Professor Trowbridge to distinguish it from civil engineering.

> The latter he defined as having to do with structures based on the principles of statical equilibrium. Such structures are passive; they are in a state of permanent rest, freedom from motion being the main object sought. In Mechanical Engineering, on the other hand, energy movement of masses in the preformance of work, construction of machinery for useful operations, are the dominant features, and hence "it embraces the entire field of Dynamical Science — the Science of Motion and Power."[83]

The degree of Dynamic Engineer was granted to students who pursued a specified graduate course after having first received the Bachelor of Philosophy

[78] Merrit C. Ternald, *A History of the Maine State College* (Orono, Maine: University of Main Press, 1916) p. 52.
[79] Earle D. Ross, *op. cit.*, p. 115.
[80] Thomas T. Reed, *op. cit.*, p. 66.
[81] *Ibid.*, p. 51.
[82] Russell H. Chittenden, *op. cit.*, p. 93.
[83] *Ibid.*, p. 151.

degree. This procedure was not usual, and like Stevens Institute of Technology, which was confined to mechanical engineering only, should be considered a special case. The other institutions developed mechanical engineering curricula alongside of civil engineering and mining, from a basic curriculum. This characteristic shows that the engineeing schools, in contrast to the practicing profession, viewed engineering as a single profession with branches whose differences were of almost incidental nature. The various curricula for the year 1870 will bear out this point. Had the profession developed the school viewpoint, it is doubtful if specialized independent societies for each branch of engineering would have developed. The engineering practice of having many branch societies was different from that of the legal and medical profession, which established single national societies to further their professional interests.

Subject Distribution.—In the engineering schools developed to provide a new type of training by new and appropriate methods the traditional college lingered, both in subject matter and instructional methods. The curricula was devised from the collegiate models, and English composition and literature, the modern languages, philosophy, political economy, mathematics and the general sciences constituted a large part of the courses of study. To illustrate this point the average percentage of time devoted in a four year course to the various subjects in the curricula of ten representative institutions for the year 1870 is given in table form. The institutions analyzed were Alabama Polytechnic Institute, Case School of Applied Science, Cornell, Illiniois, Iowa State College, Lehigh, M. I. T., Michigan, Purdue, and Wisconsin. These schools were chosen to afford a reasonable diversity of origin, status and location. What is presented is a study of the curricula of ten institutions of more than average prominence and strength rather than the ten most influential models in each field of engineering.

TABLE 3

DISTRIBUTION OF SUBJECTS OF TEN 1870 ENGINEERING SCHOOLS

	Drawing	Mech & Hydr.	Other Eng.	Eng. Maj.	Phy. Sci.	Math.	Econ. etc.	English	Foreign Languages	Phy. Mil. Sci.
	14	6	4	14	18	16	5	7	16	2
Civil Engineer	11	4	11	14	20	16	3	7	12	2
Mining Engineer	12	6	8	8	18	16	7	7	16	2
Mech. Eng.	11	5	7	12	19	16	5	7	15	2
All Curricula	23%			12%	35%			29%		
Percentage (Breakdown)										

The above table illustrates the similarity between the curricula for the three branches of engineering. Aside from twelve percent of the curriculum, which is in the various major branches, they are practically identical. The bottom row of the table shows that 29% plus 35%—or 64% of the curriculum could as well have been a part of the scientifically orientated liberal arts course. Actually this figure can be increased by 5% to 69% by adding the mechanics courses that were taught in many of the arts colleges. Girvin states that the mechanics courses stressed analytical mechanics and contained little of the mechanics of materials.

> Strength of Materials received little attention in curricula of the early engineering colleges of America until 1870. The early Mechanics texts usually devoted about a chapter of 20 or 30 pages to the theory of simple wood beams.[84]

This lack of teaching what was well developed in France could have been due to the few English texts available. The first American texts were those on bridges by Whipple in 1847[85] and by Haupt in 1859[86], which were followed by Peck's texts on Mechanics in 1870 and Wood's book on Strength of Materials in 1871.[87] These texts, together with those translated by Mahan[88] at West Point, accounted for most of the engineering texts available in English. The other texts used were written in French or German, a fact which accounts for the importance attached to foreign languages in the curriculum. These languages were taught as necesary tools rather than for mental discipline or cultural value.

Length of Course and Degrees.—As noted earlier, Rensselaer's first C.E. degree, offered in 1835, required a minimum of one year of study, while Norwich University gave the M. C. E. degree for two years' study in 1837. The general trend was to increase the degree requirements until by 1870 most of the engineering courses were four years in length, as in the ten schools whose curricula are represented in Table 3. The development of the four year program is of interest and is best illustrated by Rensselaer. This school extended its program to three years in 1850,[89] added a preparatory year in 1852,[90] and by making the preparatory year the first year of the course ended up with a four year program in 1862.[91] This kind of development was all part of adopting the American college curriculum as a model, and was still in process as

---

[84] Harvey F. Girvin, *op. cit.*, p. 235.
[85] *Ibid.*, p. 206.
[86] *Ibid.*, p. 209.
[87] *Ibid.*, p. 235.
[88] Sidney Forman, *op. cit.*, p. 58.
[89] Palmer C. Ricketts, *op. cit.*, p. 94.
[90] *Ibid.*, p. 95.
[91] *Ibid.*, p. 106.

late as 1876, when Columbia School of Mines added its preparatory year to the regular course of study to give it a four year program.[92]

The outstanding exceptions to the above practice were the Thayer School with its graduate program, Worcester with its three and a half year program, and the Sheffield Scientific School, which granted the Ph. B. degree in engineering for a three year program.[93] Yale reserved its professional engineering degrees for additional graduate work, but the commencement exercises of 1869 show one degree of C. E. as against twelve Ph. B. degrees in engineering.[94]

Using the civil engineering degree for illustrative purposes, it may be said that five varieties were conferred by the engineering schools up to 1876. These degrees, with a typical school that granted each are Rensselaer (C. E.), Lehigh (B. S.), Sheffield Scientific School (Ph. B.), Wisconsin (B. C. E.), and Washington University (B. E.). Schools not previously mentioned, with their respective degrees, are taken from the list by Richards.[95] The granting of these various types of degrees for curricula that differed but little indicates a lack of co-ordination between schools, and the absence of a strong professional society influencing educational practice. This should not be interpreted to mean that the profession was silent on the matter. Actually, the granting of a professional degree to a graduate was criticized. The following statement made in 1876 by Ashbel Welsh illustrates one such attack:

> The school confers this title when these young men graduate, and what is the result? Why they think they are engineers, and the consequence is that nine cases out of ten they never learn to be engineers.[96]

Richards, in quoting this statement, remarks that Welsh proposed that a joint committe of the American Society of Civil Engineers and the American Institute of Mining Engineers consider how to stop technical schools giving their graduates the title of "Engineer."

The Controversy of the 1870's

The Place of Practice in the Curricula.—Trautwine, in the preface to his famous *Civil Engineers Pocketbook* (1871) states:

> The writer does not include Rankine, Mosley, and Weisbach, because although their books are the productions of master-minds, and exhibit a profundity of knowledge beyond the reach of ordinary man . . . they are but little more than striking instances of how completely the

[92] A History of Columbia University, *op. cit.*, p. 357.
[93] Russell H. Chittenden, *op. cit.*, p. 357.
[94] *Ibid.*, p. 128.
[95] R. H. Richards, "American Mining Schools," *Transactions of American Institute of Mining Engineering*, Vol. XV, p. 320.
[96] *Ibid.*, p. 326.

simple facts may be buried out of sight under heaps of mathematical rubbish.[97]

The above statement reflects an attitude taken by many engineers of the 1870's toward the type of training the engineering schols of the day were providing. Clarke, in a paper before the American Society of Civil Engineers, criticized the program of the schools in these words:

Much time is wasted in our colleges and technical schools over higher mathematics. Every engineer will have to agree with me that the cases were the use of the higher calculus is indispensable are so few in our practice, that its study is not worth the time expended upon it, and we have the highest authority for saying unless its use is constantly kept up we become too rusty to use it at all. Unless the student possesses extraordinary genius for mathematics, I would limit its study to the ordinary analysis.[98]

In the same paper Clarke proposed a solution that, if adopted, would have revolutionized the system and caused the decay of the engineering schools of the time. In essence he proposed that the student attend a college, after which he would go into the field and learn the practice of his profession. Some time after gaining experience, he further suggested, if the student could spare the time he should go to a technological school. His premise was that the practice of civil engineering was specialized, and the student should know what he wanted before going to an engineering school.[99]

Clarke's paper aroused considerable controversy, with the result that a joint meeting of the American Society of Civil Engineers and American Institute of Mining Engineers was arranged, at the Philadelphia Exposition of 18-76, to discuss the question. This meeting was highlighted by Holley's paper contending that engineers should acknowledge the incomplete union between engineering science and art, and that scientific aid appeared to be more readily provided for the "practical" man than practical aid for the "scientific" man.[100]

In continuing his discussion, Holley attributed the difficulty to ignorance of the meaning of theory on the part of many practical men rather than to lack of practical courses in the schools. Holley's point of view was well received, but the discussion among the thirty-two men present was more concerned with the specific issue raised by Clarke: when shall the student take his practice; before he enters the technical school, while he is in it, or after he leaves it? To indicate the feeling of the meeting the following statements are worth repeating:

97 John C. Trautwine, Civil Engineers Pocketbook (Philadelphia, Pa.: Claxton, Remsen, and Haffelfinger, 1871) preface.
98 Thomas C. Clarke, "The Education of Civil Engineers," Transactions of the American Society of Civil Engineers, Vol. 3, 1875, p. 557.
99 Ibid., p. 558.
100 A. L. Holley, "The Inadequate Union of Engineering Science and Art," Transactions of American Institute of Mining Engineers, Vol. 4, 1876, p. 192.

I do not think it advisable, as a rule, to take the boy from the work bench and send him to school a second time. I have, in some instances, noted the effect of such a course upon young men to be disadvantageous.[101]

The introduction of a preliminary course of practical training, before the scholastic training, would be a great benefit to the schools themselves. It would weed out the hopelessly stupid or lazy or otherwise unfitted, and bring to the schools a class of young men who already know what they wanted and really wanted it.[102]

An active, ambitious, and energetic young man can rarely bring himself to the point of going back to school after having once tasted the pleasure of success in business.[103]

Richards quotes Professor Haupt's statement that a final vote at the meeting showed eight engineers in favor of practice preceding the school, twelve engineers desiring a combined theory and practice curriculum, and eight engineers preferring that practice follow graduation.[104] The above expressions suport the contention that the many engineering schools founded during the period were far from acceptable and could be expected to change as the pressures of the profession and the times exerted their influences.

[101] Coleman Setters, "Discussions on Technical Education," *Washington Meeting of American Institute of Mining Engineers,* 1876, Easton, Pennsylvania, p. 61.
[102] R. W. Richards, *op. cit.,* p. 27.
[103] R. H. Thurston, *op. cit.,* p. 33.
[104] R. W. Richards, *op. cit.,* p. 314.

chapter 6

The Period of Continued Growth and Refinement (1876-1893)

Introduction

During this period of continued growth and refinement many practices previously initiated became permanent in American engineering education. Both private and state supported institutions continued to be founded as self contained technological institutes, as mining schools, or as schools and department attached to colleges or universities. Of significance was the growth in the enrollments, in the curriculum offerings and in the resources of the schools.

The new social, economic, educational and industrial conditions provided forces that resulted in the aggregate number taking mechanical, electrical, and mining engineering being greater than those taking civil engineering. This called for new subject matter arrangements, which were organized differently by the many schools. The evolution of these many independent curricula toward a more standard type is a major phenomenon of the period.

The pattern developed by the above changes was due to institutional and regional factors rather than to the influence of outstanding individuals. This is in contrast to the manner in which the first engineering schools were developed by a few inidividuals who were ahead of their time. The outstanding educators of this period were transforming the old liberal arts college into the modern American University. This experimentation in higher education helped to lower some of the barriers that existed between classical and engineering education.

This chapter will concern itself with these many forces that have influenced the development of engineering education. The results of these forces will also be considered, together with the development of the trends established in the previous chapters. In addition to basic curriculum evolution, these trends will include professional societies, institutional structures, degrees granted, tuition costs and other considerations necessary to evaluate engineering education between the years 1876 and 1893.

115

Developments of the Period

Economic and Industrial Conditions.—The period from 1876 to 1893 began with the Philadelphia Exposition, when the country was recovering from the depression of 1873, and finished at the time of the Chicago Exposition, which coincided with the panic of 1893. During the period from 1870 to 1890 the population of the United States increased from 38,558,371 to 75,994,575.[1] In this increase it is significant that the urban population increased 123 percent while the rural population increased only 42 percent. This change accompanied an industrial expansion conducive to the development of curricula in metallurgy, mechanical engineering, and electrical engineering.

While the total population was increasing 97 percent, the annual total of basic agricultural and mineral products increased by a larger amount. Wheat production increased from 236,000,000 to 522,000,000 bushels; cotton from 4,352,000 to 10,000,000 bales; petroleum from 21,000,000 to 2,672,000-000 gallons; coal from 29,000,000 to 241,000,000 tons; and pig-iron from 1,665,000 to 13,789,000 tons.[2] Copper production increased from 500 tons in 1875[3] to 37,500 tons in 1893,[4] lead from 18,000 tons in 1870 to 139,720 tons in 1892,[5] and zinc from 700 tons in 1873 to 63,000 tons in 1890.[6]

In 1880 Hall discovered a commerical process for reducing aluminum which resulted in the American production increasing from 80 pounds in 1883 at $32 a pound to 7,500,000 pounds in 1893 at fifty cents a pound.[7] By 1882 Edison had installed over 150 electric plants in residences, hotels, mills, offices, stores and steamers.[8] In 1888, only ten years after electricity was produced commercially, there were 192,000 arc lights and 1,700,000 incandescent lights in use in the United States; 34 electric railways operating 223 cars; 49 more roads under construction, with capital being invested in various electrical services to the amount of $80,000,000 annually.[9] The railroads experienced another period of growth, with the milage increasing from 93,261 in 1880 to 167,191 in 1890.[10] As the locomotives and freight cars increased in weight many bridges had to be replaced. The New York, Pennsylvania, and Ohio Railroad Company, for instance, built 45 new bridges in Ohio alone in 1881.[11]

[1] *Historical Statistics of the United States* 1789-1945, Bureau of Census, United States Department of Commerce, p. 26.
[2] Harold Faulkner, *op. cit.,* p. 565.
[3] John Glover and William Cornell, *Development of American Industry* (New York: Prentice-Hall, 1941) p. 422.
[4] Victor S. Clark, *op. cit.,* p. 368.
[5] *Ibid.,* p. 346.
[6] *Ibid.,* p. 371.
[7] Victor S. Clark, *op. cit.,* Vol. 2, p. 368.
[8] Kerby, Washington, Darling and Kelgrow, *op. cit.,* p. 356.
[9] *American Iron and Steel Bulletin XXII,* Sept. 26, 1888, p. 293.
[10] Harold Faulkner, *op. cit.,* p. 486.
[11] Victor S. Clark, *op. cit.,* p. 244.

As the population tended to become more urban, the type of construction changed. Instead of depending almost exclusively on unskilled labor, it now required semi-skilled and skilled labor, and used large amounts of construction materials that had to be manufactured. The canal and road building of the earlier periods were replaced by the building of bridges and steel frame buildings. Between 1875 and 1890 the miles of surfaced public roads increased from 95,039 to 106,200 miles.[12] In the meantime, Roebling had built the Brooklyn bridge and Jemey had designed and constructed the first modern skyscraper for the Home Insurance Company in Chicago.[13] With these advances in urban development, industrial expansion and notable inventons, engineering education became more popular. To meet this interest new institutions were founded, established ones were enlarged, and curriculum changes made.

These changes were made in response to the new demand for graduates in the mineral industries, mechanical engineering and electrical engineering to suplement the civil engineers who had been graduated since West Point was organized in 1807.

The Supply of Secondary Students.—From 1876 to 1890, the elementary school enrollments doubled, the high school enrollments tripled, and school expenditures increased from $60,107,612 to $146,800,163.[14] For the year 1876 there were 113,000 students in 1,334 public and private secondary schools taught by 6,735 teachers.[15] Fourteen years later in 1890, the number of students had increased to 240,495 in 2,526 secondary schools.[16] These 2,526 high schools were concentrated in the larger cities and towns, leaving the rural areas with struggling school systems.[17]

Though public education was coming into its own, the number of students graduating from high school was not sufficient for the colleges of the time. In 1890 there were 14,145,663 students enrolled in all schools. Of this number 96.4 percent were in elementary grades, as compared to 2.6 percent in secondary schools and one percent in normal schools and colleges.[18] While the numbers were small, the ratio between college enrollment (151,194) and high school (370,495) would indicate that college preparation was a major function of the high school.

The concentration of the high schools in the larger cities and towns presented a problem, particularly for the colleges in the West and South. The problem was solved by the colleges operating their own preparatory courses. These preparatory courses are not to be confused with those absorbed into the

---

12 Historical Statistics of the United States, *op. cit.,* p. 220.
13 Kerby, Withington, Darling, and Kelgour, *op. cit.,* p. 320.
14 *Report of the U.S. Commissioner of Education,* 1891, p. 28.
15 *Report of the U.S. Commissioner of Education,* 1877, Vol. 2, p. XIV.
16 *Report of the U.S. Commissioner of Education,* 1892, Vol. 2, p. 694.
17 *Report of the U.S. Commissioner of Education,* 1891, p. 40.
18 *Report of the U.S. Commissioner of Education,* 1892, p. 4.

regular curriculum to make a four year program, which were previously described.

Thus the institutions were attempting to serve the people under conditions far from ideal. In 1891 Oklahoma opened without a single student qualified to undertake college work. To meet the situation a preparatory course was created, enrolling forty-five students the first semester and eighty students the second semester.[19] Another case illustrating the use of the preparatory school is given by Schmidt:

> Twenty years after its opening Wisconsin still had a rather heterogeneous student body consisting of four graduate students, eighty-three regular under-graduates, fifty-two unclassified university students and a hundred and ninety-three preparatory school pupils.[20]

The large number of preparatory students illustrates the effort made by the new institutions to realize their purpose despite some of the difficulties of the time. Another example, at the State College of Washington, shows an attempt to encourage as many as possible to enroll in the preparatory course. The first catalogue of this college lists 21 freshmen and 63 preparatory students. In order that entrance to the preparatory department might not frighten a student away, the Board of Regents passed a resolution at its meeting on December 1, 1891:

> Resolved that any person 14 years of age; and who understands arithmetic through fractions; who can distinguish the parts of speech, who can read, write and spell, reasonably grounded in geography, can enter this course (preparatory) and upon completing the course or passing satisfactory examination in it, is entitled to admission to the regular college.[21]

The New Climate in Higher Education.—In 1870 Barnard, then president of Columbia, stated the colleges had lost ground between 1838 and 1869. Enrollments decreased from one in 1,294 of the population to one in 1,929. The period mentioned was dominated by a large number of small religious colleges having fixed classical curricula, clergymen presidents, and governing boards composed thirty percent of clergymen.[22] Chapel was required, and subjects were taught for their character formation and their values as mental discipline. It would appear that the earlier attempts of Ticknor and Bancroft at Harvard, Tappan at Michigan, and Wayland at Brown, to change the college were as much ahead of their time as was the success of Nott at Union.

Following the passage of the Morrill Act a number of educational leaders

[19] Edward D. Eddy, Jr., *College of Our Land and Time* (New York: Harper & Browthers, 1947) p. 83.
[20] George P. Schmidt, *The Liberal Arts College* (New Brunswick, New Jersey: Rutgers University Prss, 1957) p. 150.
[21] Enoch A. Bryan, *A Historical Sketch of the State College of Washington* (Spokane, Washington: Inland-American Printing Company, 1928) p. 9.
[22] Earl J. McGrath, "Control of Higher Education in America," *Educational Record,* Vol. XVII (April, 1936) p. 563.

recognized the inadequacy of the traditional college and sought to adjust it to the new American social and industrial scene. In doing this they created the modern American university both by establishing new institutions and transforming existing ones. These pioneers of the new education, with their new vision and administrative skill, were not clergymen, as the old college presidents had been. The leaders were Charles Eliot of Harvard (chemist), Daniel Gilman of John Hopkins (political geography), Andrew White of Cornell (historian), William Harper of Chicago (philologist), F. A. Barnard of Columbia (chemistry and mathematics), David Jordon of Stanford (biology), G. Stanley Hall of Clark (psychologist), James Angell of Michigan (modern languages), and William Folwell of Minnesota (historian). These men, with their training in disciplines not emphasized by the traditional colleges, reversed the premises concerning the basis of education. Whereas the old curriculum started with the student and educated him without reference to the environment of his time, the new concept looked to society for its norms. With this view point, it sought to make the university part of an organic society, and to train the student to become a part of and help advance the American democratic culture into which he was born. The following quotations will illustrate this concept:

> Indeed, in all departments it is desirable that university teachers keep in touch with the outer world of literature, science, and art, and contribute not only to the progress of the arts and sciences, but also to the diffusion of knowledge among the educated public outside the confines of the university.[23]
> The brief history of modern civilization shows that in backward ages universities keep alive philosophy, and in progressive ages they lead the movement, guiding adventurous spirits to the best point of onward departure. They bring a portion of each successive generation to the confines of knowledge, to the very edge of the territory already conquered, and say to the eager youth "this far came our fathers. Now press you on!"[24]
> A university which adapts itself to urban influences, which will undertake to serve as an expression of urban civilization, and which is compelled to meet the demands of an urban environment, will in the end become something essentially different from a university located in a village or town.[25]
> "What does this country need?" (asked Gilman) "Endowments for medical science as munificent as those now provided for any branch of learning, and schools as good as those now provided in any other land." This implied the development of studies which bear upon life; such facilities as are now offorded under Huxley in London, Rolleston at Oxford,

---

[23] Charles W. Elliot, *University Administration* (Boston, Mass.: Houghlin Mifflin Company, 1908) p. 87.
[24] Charles W. Eliot, "Address at 250th Anniversary of Harvard in 1886." See S. Morison, *Three Centuries of Harvard,* p. 363.
[25] William R. Harper, *The Trend in Higher Education in America* (Chicago: University of Chicago Press, 1905) p. 158.

Foster at Cambridge, and in the best German universities. He opposed the founding of an excellent technical school recommended by Angell and White, he favored the development of a university.[26]

Leland Stanford states, "I am founding this university in the hope and belief that boys and girls can be educated into men and women prepared and willing to grapple successfully with the practicalities of life, and thus prove a blessing to themselves and to the world.[27]

The above quotations reflect much of the spirit of the Morrill Act, with the universities doing for all academic and professional divisions what the land-grant colleges were doing for mechanic arts and agriculture. Actually, the land-grant colleges and state universities became a part of, as they in part caused, this new movement in higher education. Given these similarities of purpose, it would be expected that both the engineering school and its students would enjoy the same privileges as other colleges and students of the university. As a result, the downward trend in the numbers attending liberal arts colleges reversed itself, so that all segments of higher education advanced during this period, as the following table shows.

TABLE 4

RATIO OF STUDENTS IN HIGHER EDUCATION TO EACH 1,000,000
OF POPULATION*

Year	Grad.	Grad.	Law	Medicine	Theology	Total
1876	706	9	59	191	95	1,063
1880	770	8	62	238	105	1,183
1885	687	16	53	221	110	1,087
1890	901	33	82	284	115	1,415
1893	1,087	51	107	320	113	1,678

*Report of Commissioner of Education, 1898, Vol. 2, p. 1800.

The first column includes all undergraduates in normal schools, technical schools, and colleges and universities. For the year 1876 the 706 undergraduates per million of population represent 151,971 students. In this year 22 percent of the group attended normal schools and teachers colleges, with the remaining 78 percent in the colleges, technical schools and professional schools.[29] It should be noted that as the old classical college became part of the university, the professions of law, medicine, and theology developed sepa-

[26] Abraham Flexner, Daniel Coit Gilman (New York: Harcourt, Brace and Company, 1946) p. 59.
[27] Orvin L. Elliott, Stanford University (Stanford, California: Stanford University Press, 1937) p. 16.
[28] Aubrey A. Douglas, The American School System (New York: Farrar and Rinehart, 1934) p. 4.
[29] Charles R. Mann, op. cit., p. 16.

rate graduate programs as the universities expanded vertically, while the engineering remained an undergraduate course as the university expanded horizontally.

Continuation of Institutional Trends

Additional Schools.—It is difficult to determine accurately the number of engineering schools founded up to the year 1893. Mann[30] and Barish[31] give the total number as 85; Thurston[32] as 84; Reidler[33] as 88; and Saville[34] puts it as high as 110. Reidler's figure agrees with the number of schools contained in the two lists supplied by Wellington. The first list includes 52 important schools of the time, while the second list shows institutions offering some kind of technology without having completely developed engineering schools. The difference in the number quoted could well be an index of how many of the schools of the latter type were counted as engineering schools. Regardless of the particular authority quoted, it is evident that the number of engineering schools founded between 1876 and 1893 did not approach the 63 founded between 1862 and 1876.

The fifteen to thirty schools founded between 1870 and 1893 represented institutional types that were already in existence. Case School of Applied Science (1877) and Carnegie Institute of Technology (1900), for example, were representative of private technological institutes. The University of Pittsburgh (1879) and Stanford University (1891) were private universities supporting engineering departments. South Dakota School of Mines (1883), Montana School of Mines (1883) and Michigan Mining School (1885) were typical of those schools that followed the example of Colorado School of Mines (1870). By far the largest number of institutions founded were the land-grant schools created as the various territories attained statehood. This group included the Universities of Dakota (1883), Arizona (1885), Wyoming (1886) and Idaho (1889), and the State Colleges of Oregon (1885) and Washington (1891). Two additional land-grant schools, Storrs Agricultural College and Rhode Island State College, were founded under rather unusual circumstances. The state legislatures of Connecticut and Rhode Island withdrew their land grant support from Yale and Brown Universities in 1893 and applied the money to the founding of state colleges. Yale University challenged the legislature's action, with the following result:

> In due time, the case was presented to the United States Circuit Court, and in the summer of 1895 Judge Shipman rendered his decision, justifying the claims made by the University authorities, and holding that

[30] Norman N. Barish (ed.) *Engineering Enrollment in the United States* (New York: New York University Press, 1957) p. 2.
[31] Thurston, *op. cit.*, p. 950.
[32] A. Riedler, *Report of U.S. Commissioner of Education* 1892-93, p. 666.
[33] Saville, Thorndike, *op. cit.*, p. 149.
[34] Russell H. Chittenden, *op. cit.*, Vol. I, p. 271.

the action of the state legislature in appropriating to another institution the income received by Connecticut under the act of Congress of 1862 was a direct violation of the contract made by the state in 1863.[34]

As a result of the above decision Yale was awarded damages to the amount of $154,604.45 which was equivalent to the entire land grant of 1862 plus an interest payment[35] Brown appealed its case and eventually received $40,000 for the damages it suffered.[36]

With respect to institutional structures the new mining schools followed the pattern of the Colorado School of Mines rather than the Columbia School of Mines. While Columbia retained its original name up to 1896, it operated as an institute of technology during this period. In addition to the degree of Mining Engineering, awarded in 1864, Columbia offered degrees in Civil Engineering (1869), Architecture (1881), Chemistry (1886), Metallurgy Engineering (1888), and Electrical Engineering (1889). This is one instance of the trend toward standardization that marked this period that followed the time of rapid growth in the number of schools. Another instance was the large number of schools which adopted the four year program. Of the schools in the various lists of the period, only Yale, University of Virginia, Tufts College, Worcester Polytechnic Institute, City College of New York, and the University of Missouri had three year courses. Some of these variations were more apparent than real. Yale had high entrance requirements and taught no shop courses. The University of Virginia had a six day week, and Tufts College had but a small attendance and granted the unusual degree of Bachelor of Mechanic Arts.

Professional Divisions Within the Engineering Colleges.—The industrial, social, scientific, inventive and professional forces that caused the single civil engineering curriculum was supplemented by mining and mechanical curricula prior to 1876 continued to operate up to 1893. This accounts for the new electrical and chemical engineering curricula established within the schools and the new engineering societies founded by engineers in professional practice. Basically the evolution of the electrical and chemical engineering curricula was different from that of the civil, mining, and mechanical engineering courses of study. This accounts for the following statement:

> Toward the end of the period (1876-1885) the foundation of distinct curricula in electrical engineering were laid at Massachusetts Institute of Technology and at Cornell. In both instances the new curriculum developed under the fostering of the department of physics, a further striking indication that engineering curricula evolved from the scientific toward the technical, rather than in the reverse direction as in the other branches of professional education. Fifteen years later these evolutionary

[35] *Ibid.*, p. 272.
[36] Walter C. Bronson, *op. cit.*, p. 334.

steps were repeated in the growth of distinct curricula in chemical engineering.[37]

Another case that further illustrates this evolution is described in the history of Purdue University:

> In 1887 a "school of Applied Electricity" was open to juniors and seniors as one of the special schools in Science, thereby giving further effect to the plan of President Smart to give more of an industrial character to the School of Science . . .
>
> With electricity so actively supported by the President, the logical next step was the organization in the fall of 1888 of a separate School of Electrical Engineering with Dr. Louis Bell as Professor of Physics and Applied Electricity.[38]

The establishment of electrical engineering, with its origin in the experiments of Volta, Franklin, Davey, Henry, Faraday, Morse and Edison, required an alignment with mechanical engineering. This dualism accounted for variations in departmental forms among the schools. Purdue, with its School of Electrical Engineering, granted the degree of Bachelor of Mechanical Engineering in Electrical Engineering (BME in EE) up to 1895.[39] Columbia established a two year graduate program to follow a regular four year program. It took six years to obtain an electrical engineering degree at Columbia up to 1891, at which time it was changed to four years and put on the same basis as the other curricula.[40]

An analysis of the enrollments of 26 of the largest engineering schools for the year 1892 reveals that there were 1,260 civil, 1,225 electrical, 1,471 mechanical and 241 mining engineering students.[41] Of these twenty-six schools, thirteen taught civil end electrical engineering; fourteen, mechanical engineering; and four, mining engineering. Rensselaer had 206 civil, Cornell 250 electrical, Stevens 264 mechanical, and Columbia 101 mining students; these were the schools having the largest branch enrollments. For the three year period 1890 to 1892 inclusive, there were more mechanical degrees conferred (1,119) than there were civil degrees (1,014).[42] To realize the rapid growth of mechanical engineering, these figures may be compared with the 1,048 degrees and 207 ME degrees conferred between the years 1875 and 1879. Wellington, in listing his statistics, remarks that it was difficult to separate mechanical engineering from electrical engineering since some of the best schools

37 Bulletin Number 11, "Investigation of Engineering Education," *Society for the Promotion of Engineering Education*, 1928-29, p. 546.

38 William Hepburn and Louis Sears, *Purdue University* (Indianapolis, Indiana: The Hollenbeck Press, 1925) p. 84.

39 *Ibid.*, p. 84.

40 James K. Finch, *History of School of Engineering* (New York: Columbia University Press, 1950) p. 69.

41 Some Statistics of Engineering Education, *op. cit.*, p. 107.

42 A. M. Wellington, "The School of Mechanical Engineering," *Engineering News* (Aug. 25, 1892) p. 186.

treated it as a subdivision of the regular mechanical course.[43] These figures indicate that civil engineering was losing its hold on the engineering course of study as society called for new disciplines to meet its needs. An extreme example of this was Purdue University, which had to abandon its School of Civil Engineering between 1878 and 1887 because of lack of students.

Professional Engineering Societies.—Just as the civil and mining engineers established their separate societies, similar groups were formed to represent the new engineering branches for which curricula had been developed. The American Society of Mechanical Engineers (1880), the American Institute of Electrical Engineers (1884), American Society of Naval Engineers (1888) and the American Society of Heating and Air Conditioning Engineers (1894), all had their origin in this period. In all cases these organizations were founded after a basic curriculum or subdivision of a basic curriculum representing their interest had been established within the engineering colleges.

The relationship between the schools and the engineering societies is a complicated one. In 1900 the four largest societies with the largest memberships were Civil Engineers (2,227), Mining Engineers (2,661), Mechanical Engineers (1,951), and Electrical Engineers (1,273). This total of 8,112 is small compared to the 93,956 engineers in the Census Report of that year. It might have been expected that the 8,112 engineers would be closely related to the number of engineering graduates of the time. This expectation is not borne out by the fact that in 1888 less than a quarter of the members of national engineering societies were college graduates.[44] These two factors—independent societies representing a single profession, and the large precentage of nongraduates within these organizations—are important. This combination could well explain why during this period the profession lacked a policy concerning the training of engineers.

Educational Practices and Policies

There were many and various educational practices and policies among engineering schools, whether of the same or of different organizational types. The variations were a function of such institutional factors as, for example, financial stability, age, location, and the type of industrial and educational environment of which the school was a part. The practices and policies included such details as admission requirements, teaching methods, departmental organization, types of degrees granted and tuition fees.

Admission Requiremnts.—In 1892 the United States Commissioner of Education stated that the requirements for admision to the various technological institutions were as different as the institutions themselves. In this regard he specifically said:

[43] *Ibid.,* p. 186.
[44] Bulletin No. 13, "Opinions of Professional Engineers Concerning Educational Policies and Practices," *Society for the Promotion of Engineering Education,* 1928-29, p. 36.

Through the back doors of various departments almost anyone may get admission to a university; the lower gates simply lead to the preparatory department which is most always found connected with a university. But also the requirements themselves differ greatly in different parts of the country. Schools situated in the Southern or Western States demand less.

As a rule the technological schools require no knowledge of ancient languages, except Sheffield School. Yale allows entrance at 15 years of age but the majority have fixed the lower limit of age at 16 or 17 years of age.[45]

The above statements should not be taken to imply that many of the engineering schools did not specify certain courses as necessary for admission. An analysis of the entrance requirements of 56 schools reveals that 13 subjects were required by as many as one-sixth of the schools. The following table lists these subjects, with the percentage of the schools requiring them.

TABLE 5

ENTRANCE SUBJECTS FOR 56 ENGINEERING SCHOOLS

No.	Subjects Required	No. of Schools	Percentage of 56 Schools Requiring Subjects
1	Common School Branches	54	97
2	Physical Geography	27	48.5
3	English Literature	27	48.5
4	English History	22	39.4
5	American History	45	80.5
6	French and German	15	26.8
7	Algebra Thru Quadratics	46	82
8	Plane Geometry	48	86
9	Solid Geometry	24	43
10	Elementary Physics	22	39.4
11	Elementary Chemistry	12	21.4
12	Elementary Botany	10	17.9
13	Trigonometry	8	14.2

*A. M. Wellington, "Requirements for Admission to Engineering Schools," *Engineering News* (Sept. 1, 1892) p. 210.

It will be observed that there are only four subjects that as many as 50 percent of the schools demanded, and that one of these is the common school branches. The relative strength of literature and history is indicative of the high school curricula of the time. The two schools that did not have specific requirements in the common school branches were the Missouri and Michigan

[45] Report of the United States Commissioner of Education, 1892-93, p. 659.

School of Mines. These schools examined their candidates in mathematics only.[46] Apparently there was not always a high correlation between the standing of the school and the subjects required for entrance. Rensselaer, which had high standards, required but three subjects for its entrance examination.

It should be stated that the fifty-six schools analyzed represented only the top established ones. Many of the other schools, perhaps, as many as forty, had rather lax admission requirements, owing to their newness and the undeveloped secondary school systems. Two good examples of schools of this type were the North Carolina State College, founded in 1889, and the University of Oklahoma, founded in 1892.

In July, 1889, the following rules concerning the age and qualifications of students in the above mentioned institutions was approved:

Applicants must be at least fourteen years of age; must furnish evidence of a good moral character and physical development; must be able to read and write ordinary English intelligently, and must be familiar with simple arithmetic including the practical rules of the same through fractions, and have a fair knowledge of geography and state history.[47]

Any young man or woman who has finished the course in a good country school may enter the university, and find educational work and welcome . . . (The requirements for admission were stated as "a thorough knowledge of English terminology, an ability to parse any sentence, an ability to read and interpret ordinary newspaper English composition, and ability to spell correctly and write a ready, legible hand.)[48]

The University of California and Standford University are institutions whose catalogues gave rather rigid admision specifications.

A provision for "special students" in the Berkeley requirements reads as follows: "Students who are mature—usually such as have attained their majority—and who wish to pursue some one study and its related branches, may be permitted to do so by making application through the Recorder of the Faculties." In rephrasing this for the Stanford announcement Dr. Jordan omitted the implied qualification of "maturity", but added the supposedly stricter requirement of "approval by the professor under whom the speciality was to be taken . . ."

"It has now become a fixed tradition that of all those who had the courage to make the assault not one was so far down in the scale of preparation as to fail to obtain the endorsement of some good-natured professor. And in those days there were no committees to reverse the action of the major professor."[49]

[46] A. M. Wellington, "Requirement for Admission to Engineering Schools," *Engineering News*, (Sept. 1, 1892) p. 210.

[47] David Lockmiller, *History of the North Carolina State College*, (Raleigh, North Carolina: Edwards and Broughlin Company, 1939) p. 40.

[48] Roy Biltinger, *The University of Oklahoma* (Norman, Oklahoma: Oklahoma Press, 1942) p. 16 and 17.

[49] Orrin L. Elliott, *op. cit.*, p. 96.

The above could easily be interpreted to mean that the colleges wanted an excuse to enroll almost anyone. Actually, both the students and the various faculties were very serious, as the facts indicate. Of the 255 that composed Stanford's first freshman class, 52.1 percent graduated, while North Carolina State College graduated 38 percent of its first class of fifty students.

Method of Instruction.—Henry Ward Beecher, a Harvard graduate of 1834, described what the college course of the first half of the nineteenth century stood for.

> The nearest approach to a line drawn between the common people and the aristocratic class in New England is that which educaion furnishes. And there is almost a superstitious reverence for a college educacation. If a man has been to college, he has a title. He may be of slender abilities, he may not succeed in his business but at least he has one claim to respect—he has been to college. It is like a title in a decayed family. It saves the pride and ministers pleasure to the vanity long after it has in every other respect become utterly worthless.[50]

In contrast to the above attitude, the new universities and technical schools of the late nineteen hundreds recognized the capacity of an individual to select courses that would make life meaningful to him. These institutions also adapted their programs to meet the new requirements of the times. The new concept of the student and of society required that the objectives of teaching change in a manner stated by Eliot.

> The prime object of university methods of teaching today is to make the individual student think, and do something for himself, and not merely to take in and remember other people's thoughts; to induce the students to do some thinking and acting on their own account, and not merely to hear or read about other people's doings.[51]

To accomplish the above, the pure recitation method was replaced by lectures, with periodic examinations to test the industry and accomplishments of the students. To foster student activity and participation, the lecture system was supplemented by prescribed readings, term papers, and small quizz sections conducted by junior members of the staff. The laboratory method and the theses were introduced as teaching devices in order to allow the student to correlate theory and practice through his own efforts. This practice was further extended as the engineering schools required concentrated surveying and geology courses in the field during the summer and excursions for mining students, particularly where they would observe and report on the latest industrial practices. That these methods were recognized by engineering schools which operated as a division of a university is illustrated by the following statement.

---

[50] Clarence F. Berdseye, *Individual Training in Our Colleges* (New York: The MacMillan Company, 1908) p. 80.
[51] Charles W. Eliot, *University Administration* (Boston: Houghton Mifflin Company, 1908) p. 176.

In engineering, mining, and forestry, the student obtains in his field-work much of the same sort of training which the student of botany, zoology, histology, or bacteriology gets in his laboratory. This is the reason that all universities are giving so much more attention than they formerly did to field studies for engineers in surveying, geology, and geography, to actual work in mines and metallurgical establishments for men who propose to be mining engineers, and to work in woods and lumber camps from men who propose to be foresters. This is the reason that universities are providing and carrying on summer camps for the actual conducting by students of the out-of-doors processes of these various industries. Young men cannot be initiated into the professions by the use of books, models, drawings, photographs and lantern slides alone. They must have the training of actual labor in the real laboratories of these industrial processes. To reading they must add doing in their own persons. The student of these subjects must combine study of theory with practice; and he must be personally familiar with the best applications of the soundest theories.[52]

Departmental Organization.—Aside from the differences in exterior institutional structure that developed for engineering schools, a new type of internal organization was created. The new pattern, although common to universities, colleges and technological institutions, became very strong within engineering schools. This occurred as curricula for mining, mechanical, electrical and architectural engineering were added to the civil engineering course of study.

What is referred to in the above, is the departmental form of organization that appeared in higher education in the latter part of the nineteenth century. The engineering departments, within the school, became strong as the faculties became more professional, the courses more specialized, the equipment more elaborate, and as the curricula for the various branch courses became more distinct from each other. This change also led to a separation of the mathematics and basic science courses from the engineering sciences and professional engineering courses. The subdivision of subject matter and specialization in teaching was common to all branches of learning. Finch believes its effect on higher education was as great as the creation of the American university. He also states that it was harmful to the development of unity within engineering schools. The following two quotations are his opinions on the matter.

> Certainly one of the major organizational developments of this same period (1890), almost equalling in its effect and importance the creation of a university family of schools and faculties, was the rise of the departments.[53]
> It may be argued, therefore, that the department form of university organization adopted in the early nineties led not only to the divorce of

[52] *Ibid.,* p. 195.
[53] James K. Finch, *A History of the School of Engineering of Columbia University* (New York: Columbia University Press, 1954) p. 64.

the natural science departments from engineering, but also to an unfortunate division within engineering itself.[54]

Prior to this departmental organization, the faculty was more responsible for teaching students than for the teaching of subjects. The following quotations illustrate how the faculty members taught courses in many fields before departmentalization was introduced.

Professor Herron had been with the University for eight years since 1875. Besides courses in Mathematics and Astronomy, he taught some courses in Civil Engineering, and until the coming of Professor Goss, in Mechanics as well.[55]

On May 10, 1893, O. L. Waller was elected professor of Mathematics and Civil Engineering, and Elton Fulmer, professor of Chemistry, Geology, and Mineralogy.[56]

The above statements represent the condition after forty years at one of the well established engineering schools and at the beginning period for a newly established state college. Both statements illustrate how sciences, mathematics, and engineering, were tied together prior to the departmentalization which was the basis of Finch's statement.

Types of Engineering Degrees.—The awarding of a variety of engineering degrees that developed with the founding of engineering schools continued during this period. This practice became so diverse that in 1904 no less than 63 different undergraduates and 22 different graduate engineering degrees were offered.[57] The more common of these undergraduate degrees are listed by Wellington as a result of his analysis of 60 selected colleges, and are presented in the following table:[58]

TABLE 6

TYPES OF UNDERGRADUATE ENGINEERING DEGREES CONFERRED
BY 60 COLLEGES

Degrees Conferred	No. of Colleges
C.E., M.E., E.M., etc	23
B.C.E., B.M.E., etc	11
B.E.	4
B.S.	11
B.S. in C.E., M.S., etc	9
Ph.B	2
Total	60

[54] *Ibid.,* p. 65.
[55] William M. Helpburn, and Louis M. Sears, *Purdue University* (Indianapolis, Indiana: The Hollenback Press, 1925) p. 78.
[56] Enoch A. Bryan, *op. cit.,* p. 113.
[57] Robert Fletcher, "Results Vs Ideals in Technical Education," *Science,* Vol. 30 (July 1909) p. 69.
[58] Wellington, "Degrees Conferred," *Engineering News* (Sept. 15, 1892) p. 256.

The above list does not include the degree of Bachelor of Mechanic Arts offered by Tufts College and the Bachelor of Arts degrees in various branches of engineering mentioned by Fletcher.[59] Not only were there different degrees conferred for the completion of the same basic requirements but in some cases the same degree was conferred to represent different programs. This is illustrated by using the degree of C.E. as an example. Twenty-three of the sixty colleges mentioned granted C.E. degrees as a first degree. The University of Illinois and many others granted it as a second degree to be earned after a year of post graduate study or after not less than three years of creditable practice.[60] Dartmouth and Yale conferred the C.E. degree as a graduate degree only. Thus the same degree was used as a first degree, a second degree based on professional practice, and as a graduate degree. In the field of graduate study the same confusion existed as indicated by the twenty-two different degrees that were mentioned by Fletcher. Most of these degrees can be included under the three types of M.C.E., M.S. in C.E., and C.E.

Tuition and Financial Resources.—The tuition in the private colleges and technological schools increased steadily during the nineteenth century. Despite the added costs accompanying engineering education the tuitions appear to be the same as those of the Liberal Arts Colleges of equal standing. The following comparison of the tuitions at Harvard and Rensselaer between the years 1825 and 1891 help to substantiate this point.

TABLE 7

TUITION FEES AT HARVARD AND RENSSELAER 1825 to 1891*

Years	Harvard	Rensselaer
1825-1847	90	25
1848-1863	75	60
1864-1869	104	150
1870-1891	150	200

*Palmer C. Ricketts, *op. cit.,* p. 103.

The two cases cited above are typical of the tuitions charged by a large number of the private engineering schools for the year 1891. An analysis of a study made by Wellington reveals that 24 private engineering schools had an average tuition cost of $125 a year. The three highest schools were Columbia ($205), Rensselaer ($200) and Swarthmore ($200).[61] Aside from the new Stanford, which was free, and Lehigh, which was free up to 1891, the three lowest were Cornell College of Iowa ($35), Brooklyn Polytechnic Institute ($40) and Vanderbelt ($55).

[59] Robert Fletcher, *op. cit.,* p. 69.
[60] Letter from I. O. Baker to Editor of *Engineering News* (Sept. 21, 1892).
[61] A. M. Wellington, "Cost of Technical Education," *Engineering News* (Dec. 18, 1892) p. 35.

In contrast to the tuitions charged by the privately supported colleges was the very low or no tuition of the state colleges, universities and mining schools. In this regard, of the twenty-eight institutions listed by Wellington, twelve charged some tuition while sixteen were free.[62] The twelve schools in the first category had tuition averaging $53.80. The highest tuition was $142 at the University of Virginia and the lowest tuition was $5 at Purdue University.

Aside from the cost to the student the institutions were finding out that instruction in science was more expensive than regular college teaching due to the laboratory work and the small number of students. Mann cites the case for 1868 for Massachusetts Institute of Technology and the University of Illinois.

At the Massachusetts Institute in 1868, in spite of stringent economy the total income of the school was $34,230, and the total expense $42,-650. The deficit had to be made up by subscription among the friends of the project. At this time the tuition was $100 for the first year, $125 for the second, and $150 for the third and fourth. But the total cost per student was $250 . . . . At the new Illinois Industrial University with a total income in 1869 of $35,000 and 156 students, it was $224, and there were no tuition fees.[63]

Even though both schools increased the values of their plants, annual income, and enrollment, between 1868 and 1900 they still had increasing costs per student. In 1891 Massachusetts Institute had 1,178 students, an annual income of $348,000[64] and a tuition fee of $200. Dividing the 1,178 into $348,000 gives a cost per student of $295 which is $95 more than the student paid. At the Illinois Industrial University the cost per student was $275 in 1891 based on an annual income of $483,000 and a student body of 1,756. The above costs indicate the need for private benefactors for private institutions and public support for the state schools.

Engineering Enrollments and Degrees Granted

Enrollment Material Available.—The determination of the number of students studying engineering at any one time between 1876 and 1893 is complicated by a number of factors. The reports of the commissioners of education in some instances give the numbers in scientific schools and departments without separating engineering students from agricultural, home economics, veterinary science, and pure science students. Other lists in these reports give engineering students enrolled in a selected group of schools. These lists give the distribution of enrollment between engineering branches but fail to give true totals. A third type of data available is the year to year enrollment

62 *Ibid.*, p. 35.
63 Charles R. Mann, *op. cit.*, p. 16.
64 *Ibid.*, p. 17.

of a few well known institutions. This material is helpful for estimating the rate of enrollment growth and the mortality among engineering students. These figures must be interpreted with caution, however, as during this period there were many special students in the preparatory departments that were in some cases included in the total published figures. By using a combination of these sources together with figures for the degrees granted it is possible to estimate the number of engineering students and the growth of enrollments during this period.

Number of Students Studying Science.—The Commissioner of education gives a table for the total number studying science in the United States for the period from 1880 to 1890. The figures given include engineers but do not distinguish them from other science students. This table is reproduced below and gives some valuable figures as to the distribution of students between private and land-grant colleges.

TABLE 8

SCIENCE AND ENGINEERING STUDENTS AT VARIOUS TYPES OF COLLEGES 1880-1890*

Date	All Stud. Science	Non Land-Grant Tech. Colleges	Sci. Dept. Colleges	Land-Grant Colleges	Degrees Science
1880-81	14,300	5,700	4,400	4,300	1,100
1881-82	16,600	7,200	4,400	4,700	1,100
1883-84	16,100	7,600	4,400	4,300	1,100
1884-85	17,600	8,500	4,600	4,400	1,170
1885-86	16,400	7,800	4,700	3,900	1,130
1886-87	17,800	7,900	5,600	4,300	1,170
1889-90	....	....	7,900	6,200	1,190

Report of the Commissioner of Education, 1889-90, Vol. 2.

The above table indicates that approximately one-fourth of the science students were in land-grant colleges, another fourth in science departments of Liberal Arts Colleges, and the remaining half in schools of technology. It should also be noted that the ratio of the total number of students enrolled to the number graduating is approximately 15 to 1.

An Approximation of Student Enrollment.—There are no data to be found in the literature on engineering education giving total engineering enrollments for the years covering this period between 1876 and 1893. An approximation will be worked out to compare with the approximate 1,400 students enrolled in 1870.[65] The bases of this approximation rests upon three proportions. The first of these is that 60.5 percent of the science students in land-

[65] Norman N. Barish (ed.) *op. cit.,* p. 2.

grant colleges for the year 1884 were studying engineering.[66] The second percentage is obtained from the enrollment figures of the Massachusetts Institute of Technology as obtained from catalogues for the years 1876 to 1893. These figures show that of the total enrollment 30 percent were special students and 70 percent were taking the regular course. This percentage was obtained by not counting the students in the two year School of Mechanic Arts or in the Lowell Institute Evening School which were peculiar to the Institute. The third ratio is the fifteen to one factor between students and graduates to which reference has already been made.

By referring back to Table 8 it will be seen that the total science enrollment of 17,800 for the year 1886-87 is in (1) Land-Grant Colleges; (2) Science Departments of Colleges and (3) Technological Institutes. By assuming that the 9,900 students in the first two groups are 60.5 percent engineers of whom 70 percent are regular students we have 4,193 students. If we add to this 70 percent of the 7,900 engineers in the Technological Institutes we have another 5,530 or a total of 9,723 engineering students.

The above value is approximate but may be justified by another approach. The number of degrees granted from 74 engineering schools for the year 1889 was 664.[67] By multiplying this number by fifteen an under-graduate enrollment of 9,960 is obtained. This number of fifteen is the 15 to 1 ratio previously mentioned. The closeness of the results from these independent approaches justifies the estimate that in the late 1880's the engineering enrollment in the United States was approximately 10,000 students. This figure could well be on the low side as there were more schools graduating engineers than the seventy-four cited by Thurston. It is also very likely that more than 60.5 percent of the students in the science departments of the non-land grant colleges and universities were in engineering. The majority of these colleges and engineering departments had one hundred or fewer students divided between civil, mechanical, electrical, and mining engineering. Of the total number of students in 1892-93, 3,876 were enrolled in as few as eighteen of the larger schools leaving the remainder for the approximately seventy other engineering schools and departments.

Student Mortality.—From the figures available it is impossible to determine the actual elimination of students as the difference between the number of graduates in any year and the number of freshmen four years back does not indicate the true mortality. The class enrollments do not allow for those who entered with advanced standing or for those who were retarded for a year or more. Not being able to follow through an actual freshmen class resort was made to the catalogues of the Massachusetts Institute of Technology and table 9 gives the enrollments by classes from 1876 to 1891. For each class

[66] *Report of the U.S. Commissioner of Education*, 1895, Vol. 2, p. 1201.
[67] Robert Thurston, *op. cit.*, p. 950.

there are two columns, the first giving the student enrollment and the second the percentage retained in the class as compared to the number that enrolled as freshmen one, two or three years ago as the case may be.

TABLE 9

DISTRIBUTION OF ATTENDANCE IN MASSACHUSETTS INSTITUTE OF TECHNOLOGY 1870-1892

Year	Freshman		Sophomore		Junior		Senior	
	No.	%	No.	% of orig. Fresh.	No.	% of orig. Fresh.	No.	% of orig. Fresh.
1876	36	100	42	63	23	63	33	49
1877	49	100	17	47.5	29	44	22	61
1878	36	100	31	63	13	36	23	35
1879	37	100	29	81	34	69	9	25
1880	62	100	20	54	27	75	31	63
1881	87	100	33	53	20	54	24	67
1882	114	100	57	65	29	47	19	51
1883	145	100	61	53	37	55	29	47
1884	193	100	85	58	60	62	30	34
1885	187	100	112	58	63	43	53	46
1886	198	100	98	52	87	45	57	39
1887	237	100	124	63	78	41	79	41
1888	251	100	144	61	120	61	74	40
1889	261	100	148	59	130	55	110	56
1890	250	100	154	59	138	55	114	48
1891	263	100	155	62	140	54	146	58
Total		100		59.5		53.7		47.5

An analysis of table 9 reveals that the major elimination of approximately forty percent took place between the freshmen and sophomore classes. An examination of the curriculum would show the students were eliminated before having had contact with any appreciable amount of engineering. The freshman program consisted of English, Languages, Mathematics, Chemistry and Drawing. Apparently those who could survive the general studies had a good chance of graduating; 80 percent of the sophomore class finished. A study of the table would lead one to believe that this figure is high with respect to the actual students who started the freshman year. The fact that the size of the senior class is in many cases very little different from the junior class suggests that some transfer students were involved.The enrollment figures given in the table do not represent all the students in attendance at the Institute. Counting the graduate students, the special students and those in the two year School of

Mechanic Arts, there were half again as many students. This is mentioned to indicate that the public served by the Institute represented a wider interest than it did at a later date.

To compare the data for the Massachusetts Institute of Technology with corresponding figures for land-grant colleges table 10 is presented. The table is not complete as data for the year 1882 were not available.

TABLE 10

DISTRIBUTION OF ATTENDANCE IN LAND-GRANT COLLEGES
1880-1885*

Year	Freshman		Sophomore		Junior		Senior	
	No.	%	No.	%	No.	%	No.	%
1880	1170	100	850	----	560	----	520	----
1880	1820	100	970	82	620	----	460	----
1882	--------	------	------	----	------		- ---	
1883	1560	100	830	----	520	28	390	33
1884	1610	100	900	49	560	----	400	22
1885	1550	100	760	41	480	26	315	----

*Report of the U.S. Commissioner of Education, 1889 p. 867.

The incompleteness of the table and the few years covered do not warrant average values for comparison purposes. What is given, however, does justify the statement that there was a great drop between the freshmen and sophomore years. Unlike the Institute, however, the elimination in the land-grant colleges continued to a considerable degree during the junior and senior years. It is not safe to say that approximately seventy percent failed because they did not graduate. Actually many other factors such as health, finances, interest in work, and attitude of faculty enter into the picture. From the differences between the enrollment characteristics of both types of institutions it would appear that there was no national pattern concerning mortality among engineering students.

With respect to the land-grant colleges it should be stated that they were being critized for reaching out somewhat further than the law allowed.[68] In the report of the Commission of Education for 1890-91 we find:

> That the leading object of these institutions shall be to teach such branches of learning as are related to agriculture and mechanic arts; but not even the most cursory examination of the colleges thus aided will show that in a large majority of cases these branches have not been made the leading objects, although of late years they have been more and

68 I. L. Kanel, op. cit., p. 101.

more demanding greater recognition, as at least coordinate departments of the several institutions.[69]

A discussion of this topic will be reserved for the next chapter as the data supplied on enrollments for the period after 1900 are better classified to show the percentage of students enrolled in the various divisions of the land-grant colleges.

Engineering Curricula

General Curricula Considerations.—In the curricula development of the period, there was an attempt to meet the profession's need without any standard pattern being supplied by the profession. This resulted in a number of different combinations originating from two principal sources. One curricula imitated those of the established schools while the second was more individualistic, and sought to meet specific local needs. Regardless of the differences practically all the curricula had much in common. These similarities consisted of: (1) an almost uniform freshman year; (2) a four year course; (3) an increase over the year 1870 in the hours of technical subjects taught to the sacrifice of the humanities; (4) an enlarged laboratory program; (5) a required thesis; (6) a core of subjects consisting of humanities, mathematics, physical sciences, engineering sciences and drawing common to all curricula. On the other hand,there was a practice in many schools of subdividing the professional side of the curriculum. This resulted in the civil engineer specializing in such options as topographical, hydraulic, railway or construction engineering. In like manner the mechanical engineer could specialize in machine design, steam power or marine engineering.

TABLE 11

DISTRIBUTION OF SUBJECTS FOR TEN ENGINEERING SCHOOLS FOR THE YEAR 1885

| | Engineering | | | | Eng. Sci. | Sci.&Math | | Human | | Phy Ed. |
	Maj.	Other Eng.	Draw.	Shop	Mech &Hyd.	Phy. Sci.	Math	Hist. Lit.	Elec.	Mil.Sci.
Civil Eng.	27	3	10	0	10	12	15	17	3	3
Mining Eng.	21	15	13	0	3	15	13	17	0	3
Mech. Eng.	18	3	12	12	7	9	16	20	1	2
Elec. Eng.	20	13	7	7	8	11	14	17	1	2
All Eng.	22	8	10	5	7	12	15	18	1	2
All Eng.	30		10	5	7	27		18	1	2

*Revolutionary Trends in Engineering Curricula, *op. cit.,* pp. 527 to 532.

[69] *Report of the U.S. Commission of Education,* 1890-9-.

Distribution of Subject Matter Within Engineering Curricula.—To record the practice and provide an element illustrating the evolutionary trend in engineering curricula table 11 is presented. This table contains data from the same ten engineering schools used in making table 1 which supplied data for the year 1870. The data for both these tables were obtained from scaling bar charts presented in pages 527 to 532 of a study made by the Society for the Promotion of Engineering Education.

The comparison between the curricula for 1870 and 1885 are of interest and the decrease in the time alloted the humanities from 29 to 18 percent practically equals the increase of 12 to 22 percent for the major engineering subjects. The data indicates a shift away from the original liberal arts curriculum upon which the 1870 curriculum was based. By combining the humanities and the mathematics and physical sciences the total for 1885 is 45 percent of the curricula as compared to 64 percent for 1870. Thus the structure was no longer the scientifically orientated classical curriculum of the liberal arts college but a course of study of its own utilizing the science, mathematics and humanity departments of the arts college. Of further interest in the comparison of tables 1 and 11 is the slight decrease in drawing and the large amount of shop courses for the mechanical and electrical engineers in 1885. The complete rigidness of the curricula evidenced by the one percent of electives is difficult to explain at a time when the elective system was popular in the liberal arts college.

The Professional Schools.—An examination of some of the catalogues of the time reveals that the majority of the engineering courses stressed the art of engineering and used problems and methods directly applicable to practice. Examples of such courses in civil engineering are hydraulics, water supply, water motors, pumps and pumping machinery, sewerage and drainage, railway construction, railway management, bridges, framed structures, masonry structures, structures of wood and foundations. Corresponding courses for mining were assaying and blow-piping, tunnelling, ore dressing, blast furnaces, smelting, metallurgy and mining law. For the field of mechanical engineering there were steam engines, valve gears, boilers and furnaces, tests of power, machine design, locomotive construction, mill engineering and shop work. The electrical engineering course was a combination of the basic engineering core with additions from physics and mechanical engineering. Even as late as 1890 the electrical course at Massachusetts Institute of Technology contained no professional subjects until the senior year. These courses had rather general titles such as, technical applications of electricity to telegraph, telephones and electric lighting. The chemical engineering curriculum was also closely associated with the mechanical course as the 1890 notice in the Massachusetts Institute of Technology catalogue of that year states:

Chemical Engineering.—This course is arranged to meet the needs of students who desire a general training in mechanical engineering, and who wish to devote a portion of their time to the study of the applications of chemistry to the arts, especially to those engineering problems which relate to the use and manufacture of chemical products.

Some Particular Engineering Curricula.—The average percentages given in Table 11 do not cover many individual cases, even though they do agree with a corresponding study by Wellington.[71] One interesting deviation from the average is the curricula of the University of Wyoming for the year 1890-91. This course of study reflects the inadequate secondary schools of the times by having trigonometry taught as late as the last term of the sophomore year. The following schedule also stresses the engineering sciences and the humanities with a minimum of professional courses of the applied type.

TABLE 12

MECHANICAL ENGINEERING COURSE OF STUDY AT UNIVERSITY OF WYOMING

Freshman Year				
Fall Term	Algebra	Rhetoric	Physics	Freehand Drawing	Elocution
Winter Term	Algebra	Bookkeeping	Physics	Freehand Drawing	Elocution
Spring Term	Plane Geom	Bookkeeping	Rhetoric	Mech. Drawing	Rhetorical Work

Sophomore Year				
Fall Term	Plane Geom	French or German	Physics	Mech. Drawing	Rhetorical Work
Winter Term	Solid Geom.	French or German	Descriptive Geometry	Mech. Drawing	Rhetorical Work
Spring Term	Trig.	French or German	Surveying	Mech. Drawing	Rhetorical Work

Junior Year				
Fall Term	Differential Calculus	French or German	Inorganic Chemistry	Mech. Drawing	Rhetorical Work
Winter Term	Integral Calculus	French or German	Chemistry Test & Metals	Analytical Geometry	Rhetorical Work
Spring Term	Analytical Mechanics	French or German	Mechanics of Materials	Kinematic Drawing	Rhetorical Work

Senior Year				
Fall Term	Analytic Mechanics	English Literature	Thermo-dynamics	Elements of Mechanics	Rhetorical Work
Winter Term	Steam Engines	Astronomy	Machine Design	Machine Drafting	Thesis Work
Spring Term	Electricity & Magnetism	Hydraulics	Lab in Engineering	Thesis Work	

[71] A. M. Wellington, "Distribution of Work of Instruction," *Engineering News* (Oct. 6, 1892) p. 327.

A second curriculum of special interest is that offered by the University of Tennessee in Mechanical Engineering for the year 1890. This scheme made applied mechanics a prominent feature without offering the applied courses that the Masachusetts Institute of Technology and the Alabama Polytechnic Institute did. A striking characteristic of the curriculum was that absolutely no cultural courses were offered in the last three years. On the basis of this it would have been expected to have had room for more applied courses. The reason it did not have them is that it offered only five courses the first semester and four courses the second semester of the senior year as compared to the nine offered by the Massachusetts Institute each semester.

TABLE 13

MECHANICAL ENGINEERING OF UNIVERSITY OF TENNESEE 1890

Sophomore Year	Hours Per Week	
	1st Term	2nd Term
Trigonometry, Analytical Geometry, Calculus	5	5
Descriptive Geometry, Mechanics	2	2
Chemistry	3	5
Drawing	3	3
Shop Work	3	3
Military Tactics	1	1
Junior Year		
Determinants, Calculus, Least Squares, Mathematics	3	3
Theoretical Mechanics	3	3
Kinematics, Mechanics	3	--
Materials Mechanics	--	3
Physics	3	3
Drawing	3	3
Shop Work	3	3
Senior Year		
Theoretical Mechanics	5	--
Prime movers, Mechanics	2	--
Physics	3	3
Machine Designing	3	3
Machine Construction, Mechanic Arts	3	--
Expert work, Mechanic Arts	--	6
Thesis	--	--

The last specific example to be presented is that of the Civil Engineering curricula of the University of Arizona for the year 1890. This is presented to illustrate how the curricula was adapted to the farming community that had to deal with irrigation as a major problem. The last two years of this course show the prominence given to hydraulic practice specifically adapted to the problems within the state.

TABLE 14

JUNIOR AND SENIOR YEARS OF CIVIL ENGINEERING CURRICULA AT THE UNIVERSITY OF ARIZONA FOR 1890

Junior Year

Winter Term	Spring Term
Higher Algebra	Analytical Geometry
Chemistry of Soils	Physics
Geology	Irrigation Hydraulics
German	Hydraulic Practice
Drawing	German

Senior Year

Fall Term	Winter Term	Spring Term
Calculus	Form & Irrigation Laws	Canals, reservoirs
Meteorology	Hydraulics	Political Economy
Astronomy	Calculus	Strength of Materials
Hydraulics	Constitutional History	German
Hydraulic Practice	Engineering Practice	Field Practice
German	German	

Changes in Established Patterns

As the curricula evolved, accompanying the increase in enrollment and number of schools, some new characteristics appeared in engineering education. These innovations included graduate study, the recognition of research, the undergraduate thesis, the founding of Tau Beta Pi, and the organizing of the Society for the Promotion of Engineering Education. Aside from the thesis, the impact of these changes was not strong up to 1893. They deserve attention, however, because during this period their beginnings were made in answer to a variety of forces. For the most part the stronger components of these forces resided in other segments of the higher educational system, that were borrowed and carried over into engineering education to meet its own status needs. Once started in this fashion they developed more rapidly in the early years of the twentieth century in response to stimuli that were strongest outside of the institutions themselves.

Graduate Study and Research.—Prior to 1893 graduate study and research occupied a small place in American engineering education. The forces responsible for their beginnings were strong while the conditions necessary for rapid growth were not present until a later period. Influences causing the start were the rapid acceptance of the practice in other segments of higher education, and the government support for agricultural research given under the Hatch Act of 1887 to Land-Grant colleges. The slowness of developing graduate study was due at least in part, to social-economic conditions in society and the lack of faculty who were trained and experienced in research.

Although the first American degree of Doctor of Philosophy was granted by Yale in 1861 it remained for the creation of the modern American University by such men as Gilman of John Hopkins, Eliot of Harvard, Angell of Michigan, White of Cornell, Hall of Clark, Folwell of Minnesota, James of Illinois and Butler of Columbia before graduate education and research had a strong place in higher education in America. Under the leadership of such men the graduate enrollment in the United States increased 900 percent between 1876 and 1893 while corresponding undergraduate increases were 40 percent. These figures are based upon a numerical graduate enrollment increase from 400 students in 1875 to 3600 students in 1893.[72] For the year 1893, there were 195[73] doctor's degrees conferred in course and for the year 1890 there were 1,135 master's degrees conferred in course.[74] These figures illustrate the rapid growth and strength of the graduate programs in the American universities for this period. It should be mentioned that caution should be exercised in evaluating the strnegth of the program on the basis of advanced degrees awarded unless they are specified as having been granted for academic work completed. As late as 1893 there were 396 A.M., 16 M.S. and one Ph.D. degrees awarded on an honorary basis.[75]

The above discussion is presented to illustrate the new climate in higher education that provided a stimulus for graduate work in engineering. Actually the engineering schools lagged behind the other divisions of the universities in the development of graduate work. Only six engineering institutions conferred advanced degrees in engineering prior to 1890 with only three earned doctorates being conferred up to the year 1896.[76] The reason for the American fertility in technology with the accompanying sterility in the development of abstract theoretical laws during this period is of interest to speculate upon. In this regard Curti states:

> Their inventiveness (American) was attributed to the Yankee's moral flair for improving not only his mind and character but the tools he used; to the fact that a continent was to be civilized by inadequate manpower, with the result that a premium was not put on the invention of time saving devices; and to the probability that the creative impulse which in some socoieties expressed itself in the fine arts found outlets in America in mechanical inventions.[77]

Another explanation advanced by Tocqueville as early as 1840 supplies another view point worth mentioning. He suggested that in Europe, where a

[72] Report of U.S. Commission of Education, 1892-93, Vol. I, p. 78.
[73] Ibid., p. 84.
[74] John C. Walton, "Graduate Study in Universities and Colleges in the United States," U.S. Department of Interior Bulletin No. 20, 1934, p. 13.
[75] Report of U.S. Commission of Education 1892-93, Vol. I, p. 84.
[76] Norman, N. Barish, op. cit., p. 3.
[77] Merle Curti, The Growth of American Thought (New York: Harper Brothers, 1943) p. 338.

permanent inequality of conditions prevailed, men confined themselves to the arrogant and sterile researches of abstract truths, whilst the social conditions and institutions of democracy prepared them to seek immediate and useful practical results of the sciences.[78]

Graduate Study and Research in Land-Grant Colleges.—Under the Morrill Act of 1862 Agriculture and the Mechanic Arts were on an equal basis. Up to the year 1900 the ratio of engineering to agricultural students was 5 to 1 in favor of engineering.[79] Despite the large number of engineering students it was agriculture that received federal support. In 1862 the United States Department of Agriculture was established without there being a Department of Mechanic Arts founded. In 1887 the Hatch Act was passed for the organization and support of Agricultural experiment stations under the control of the land-grant colleges. No provisions were made for engineering experiment stations with federal support. The Association of Land-Grant Colleges and Universities was established in 1885. From the time of its organization up to its seventh annual convention in 1893 no mention is made in its proceedings of engineering or mechanic arts.[80] All of these factors were favorable for stimulating graduate study and research in agriculture rather than in engineering. This accounts for the fact that while the engineering undergraduate enrollment was five times that of agriculture only twenty-seven[81] of the two-hundred and forty-one[82] master's degrees awarded by land-grant colleges in 1890 were in engineering.

Tau Beta Pi and Sigma Xi Societies.—The establishment of Tau Beta Pi at Lehigh University in 1885 and of Sigma Xi at Cornell University in 1885, signified a spirit of refinement and quality in engineering education. Although started, their influence during this period was small. Aside from the Lehigh chapter, Michigan Agricultural College (1892) was the only other college to organize a Tau Beta group.[83] The only two technological schools that had Sigma Xi chapters were Rensselaer and Case institutes. There were, in addition, twenty-two chapters at other institutions that supported departments or schools of engineering.[84]

It is of interest that the above societies were academic from the dates of their founding. This differed from the Phi Beta Kappa which was founded as a social club at William and Mary College in 1776. It was not until 1826 that the Phi Beta Kappa became academic at which time it had additional chapters

---

[78] Alexis de Tocqueville, *Democracy in America* (London: 1840) Vol. III, p. 89.
[79] Survey of Land-Grant Colleges and Universities, *op. cit.,* Vol. I, p. 799.
[80] *Ibid.,* p. 799.
[81] *Ibid.,* Vol. 1, p. 809.
[82] *Ibid.,* Vol. 2, p. 719.
[83] R. C. Matthews, "The Tau Beta Pi Associations," *Society for the Promotion of Engineering Education,* Vol. XV, 1907, p. 303.
[84] Henry B. Ward, "Sigma Xi in Scientific Education," *Society for the Promotion of Engineering Education,* Vol. XV, 1907, p. 288.

at Harvard (1781), Dartmouth (1789), Union (1817) and Bowdoin (1826).

A National University.—Interest in the establishment of a national university had roots as old as the government itself. George Washington made provisions in his will and the first six presidents had recommended such an institution more or less warmly.[85] President Grant recommended the subject to Congress in 1873, as did President Hayes in 1877 and 1878. The action of Congress in 1873 was a bill providing for a university at Washington endowed by Congress to the amount of $20,000,000 yielding five percent interest to be used for the general purpose of that institution.[86] It is of interest that this movement continued to be strong as late as 1893 when the nation's educational needs were so well supplied by both pirvate and state instituiions.

R. H. Thurston, the director of mechanical engineering at Cornell University, devoted eleven of his 147 page article on technical education to the cause of a national university.[87] Two other bills cited by Hinsdale are of interest. The first was submitted in 1890 to the United States Senate under the title "A Bill to Establish the University of the United States," and the second in 1892 entitled "A Bill to Establish a National University."[88] Both of these bills were presented when Congress had founded the Natural Museum, the Library of Congress, the National Observatory and the Bureau of Education, which in some sense took the place of a university. Reed points out that they did not secure support as a national school could not adapt itself to local needs and would not provide the healthy rivalry so necessary among institutions.

[85] B. A. Hensdate, "American Educational History," *Report of the U.S. Commissioner of Education,* 1892-93, Vol. II, p. 1311.
[86] House Report No. 89, Forty-Second Congress, Third Session.
[87] R. N. Thurston, *op. cit.,* p. 855 to 1022.
[88] B. A. Hensdate, *op. cit.,* p. 1312.

chapter 7

Period of Evaluation (1893-1907)

Introduction

The year 1893 marked the beginning of an important period for engineering education. The Society for the Promotion of Engineering Education was founded at the World's Columbia Exposition held at Chicago. This Exposition was described by Henry Adams as the first expression of American thought as a unity.[1] Anderson contrasted it with the London Exhibition of 1851, which marked the beginning of technical education as the Chicago Exposition marked the beginnings of the technical movement of which we are now a part.[2] This movement, the ascendency of the industrial over the agricultural economy, was definitely settled by 1896.

Whether measured in terms of working population, income, wealth or exports, agriculture's contribution to the economy had greatly decreased since the Civil War, and by 1896 agriculture's dominant position had been irretirevably lost.[3] The year 1896 as a turning point is mentioned by Drummond[4] and well described by McGrane:

> It was not the personal magnetism of the republican candidate, William McKinley, nor the organizing genius of his campaign manager, Marcus A. Hanna, that was responsible for the defeat of Bryan. Bryan was stopped by the new industrialism that had developed since the Civil War, and with his defeat the American agrarian order was submerged.[5]

The new industrialism was proud of its technical educational system, and engineering education no longer had to justify itself or defend its position as a division of higher education. In fact, it took pride in its status to the extent that Baker in 1900 comments that "It was generally conceded that the Amer-

[1] Henry Adams, *The Education o fHenry Adams,* (New York: The Modern Library, Inc., 1931) p. 343.
[2] Victor C. Anderson, "Progress in Technical Education," *Society for the Promotion of Engineering Education,* Vol. XVIII, 1905, p. 133.
[3] Howard R. Smith, *op. cit.,* p. 411.
[4] Dwight L. Drumond, *America in Our Times,* (New York: Henry Holt & Company, 1947) p. 72.
[5] Reginald C. McGrane, *op. cit.,* p. 454.

ican Engineering School in equipment, methods, and scope of instruction was superior to that of any European school, at least for American engineers."[6] Practically the identical statement was made at a later date (1900), with the addition that the same claim could not then be made for much of the theoretical instruction and especially for the instruction in design.[7]

With the attitude of the schools on having arrived, the emphasis of the period concentrated on an evaluation and refinement of the already established operations of engineering education. With few exceptions there were no new curricula, institutional types or instructional methods adopted, while the enrollments increased mainly by the enlargement of already existing institutions. Exceptions to the general trend were the establishment of cooperative education and engineering experiment stations. Outside of the schools, there was the increase both in number and size of professional societies. There was also Wellington's attack on the number and methods of the mining schools.

All of the above topics will be considered up to the year 1907 in the framework of the industrial, social and education forces that acted upon them. The year 1907 is taken as the end of the period for reasons well expressed by Turneauve:

> There appear to be reasons why there will be less strenuous growth in numbers and in material equipment; that in some respects, the technical schools of the country have reached a condition of comparative stability, and during the next decade are likely to develop along other lines.[8]

Developments of the Period

Industrial Expansion.—Despite the depression of 1893, the United States was emerging as a world power during the decade from 1890 to 1900. In this period the steel production increased 300 precent[9] and the valuation of all property changed from 65,037 to 88,517 million dollars.[10] In 1906 the country produced half of the world's copper[11] and had blast furnace outputs surpassing those of Germany, England and France.[12] In 1895 the Niagara power plant went into operation and by 1905 some 175 textile mills used electricity for driving their machinery.[13]

6 Ira O. Baker, "Engineering Education in the United States At the End of the Century," *Society for the Promotion of Engineering Education,* Vol. VIII, 1900, p. 21.
7 Bulletin No. 11, "Investigation of Engineering Education 1923-1929," *Society for the Promotion of Engineering Education,* p. 548.
8 Frederick E. Turneauve, "Recent Developments and Present Tendencies in Technical Education," *Society for the Promotion of Engineering Education,* Vol. XVII, 1909, p. 19.
9 Reginald C. McGrane, *op. cit.,* p. 437.
10 *Historical Statistics of the United States,* 1789-1945, p. 10.
11 Victor S. Clark, *op. cit.,* Vol. III, p. 1
12 H. M. Boyleston, *Iron and Steel* (New York: John Wiley and Sons, 1928) p. 20.
13 Victor S. Clark, *op. cit.,* Vol. III, p. 2.

With the development of farm machinery, machine tools, industrial equipment, automobiles, household conveniences, and other manufacturing products, the question of markets became relatively more important than individual patents and inventions.[14] It was a time when emphasis on practicality was given strong impetus by the expansion of all things useful. Writing in 1906, Thwing lamented, "The altar fires of creative imagination are burned out, and in their place are the fires of steamship boilers and the mogul locomotives."[15] In the same vain Henry Adams describes his reaction to the Saint Louis Exposition of 1904:

> The new American showed his parentage proudly; he was the child of steam and the brother of the dynamo, and already, within less than thirty years, this mass of mixed humanity, brought together by steam, was squeezed and welded into shape; a product of so much mechanical power and bearing no distinctive marks but that of pressure.[16]

In the process of evolving this pattern, similar industries located in common areas, labor organized, management separated from ownership, and urban growth accelerated. Despite this accent on specialization, in geographical areas, engineering education became national in its aims and methods. With the exception of some mining schools and textiles curricula, few institutions catered to specific area needs. The schools throughout the country had essentially the same curricula designed to meet national rather than local opportunities.

TABLE 15

GENERAL EDUCATION CHANGES BETWEEN 1894 and 1910

Year	Population	Students in Secondary Schools		No. of Col. and Univ.	Total Students in Col. & Univ.
		Number	% Publ.		
1894	67,900,000	408,000	71	476	143,600
1910	91,972,000	1,032,000	88	492	275,200
% Increase	35.5	150	18	3.3	91

[14] Ibid., p. 146.
[15] Edward Eddy, op. cit., p. 113.
[16] Henry Adams, op. cit., p. 466.

TABLE 16

CHANGES IN PROFESSIONAL EDUCATION BETWEEN 1890-1910*

Year	Population	No. of Law Schools & Students	No. of Med. Schools & Students	No. of Theo. Schools & Students	No. of Eng. Schools & Students
1890	64,948,000	16 (4,518)	133 (15,488)	145 (7,093)	85 (10,000)
1910	91,972,000	124 (19,569)	131 (21,394)	184 (11,012)	108 (30,300)
% Increase	41.8 %	103 (360)	—1.5 (38.1)	26.8 (55.4)	27 (203)

*Alfred Z. Reed, "Training for the Public Profession of the Law," Bulletin No. 15, Carnegie Foundation For the Advancement of Teaching, New York, 1921, p. 443.

Educational Growth of the Period.—The numerical changes in various components of the American educational system are presented in Tables 15 and 16. The data used for Table 15 are obtained from the Statistical Abstracts and from the reports of the Commissioner of Education for the years reported; because of the difficulty of obtaining data for the year 1907, the year 1910 is used as the terminal date.

Tables 15 and 16 reveal that all segments of the educational system, with the exception of medical education increased faster than the population. Of particular interest are these facts: (1) that secondary school enrollment outstripped the population by over 400 percent, almost exclusively because of the growth of the public high school; (2) that the college and university enrollment almost doubled by increasing the enrollments of the already established colleges; (3) that within the professional classification, the law schools and law enrollment had the greatest growth, with engineering education in second place. Both these growths reflect the needs of the industrial expansion. Other figures of interest, obtained from the same sources, reveal that the amount spent on public education increased 133 percent while the private benefactions for higher education gained 107 percent.

Engineering education recognized the role the expanded public high school should assume, as the following typical quotation illustrates:

> The curriculum of the secondary school must be broadened. The demand for it comes from new constituencies with increasing emphasis each year. Secondary education is rapidly becoming universal, and its form and content must take into account new fields for educated people. The curriculum must adopt itself to modern requirements. It must touch modern life, modern conditions, modern forces, modern responsibilities.

We want living languages and living issues. We must teach the duties of the American citizen rather than the manner of life of a slave owner in Athens.[17]

The Land-Grant Colleges.—The last chapter contained a statement from the Commissioner of Education for 1891 to the effect that the land-grant colleges were fast extending their activities beyond what the law allowed. Table 17 gives the enrollment figures in those divisions that the Commissioner must have interpreted as being land-grant functions. Compared to the total enrollments, these figures are not large.

TABLE 17

LAND-GRANT COLLEGE ENROLLMENTS 1903-1907*

	1903	1904	1905	1906	1907
Agriculture	2,461	2,331	2,473	2,903	3,930
Domestic Science	637	674	717	833	1,030
Mechanic Arts	10,535	12,236	13,000	13,937	15,896
Special Courses	5,485	5,658	5,131	6,420	7,776
All Departments	44,719	40,435	48,593	54,974	56,548

*Report of the U.S. Commissioner of Education, Vol. II, 1910, p. 980.

Using the year 1903 as an example, the so-called land-grant functions account for 19,119 students or 43 percent of the total enrollment of 44,719. If the commissioner used figures similar to these to justify his statement, he interpreted the land-grant act very narrowly. Basically it had been admitted from the start that the name Mechanic Arts and Agriculture was unfortunate. Actually the wording of the bill was broad:

. . . the endowment, support, and maintenance of at least one college where the leading object shall be, without excluding other scientific or classical studies, . . . in order to promote the liberal and practical education of the industrial classes in the several pursuits and professions of life.[18]

In the spirit of the above statement of the act, we find Eddy discussing the land-grant colleges of 1906 as "The curriculum began to reflect society and society's needs in a much greater fashion than ever before."[19] After explaining that the colleges could no longer operate on their land grant endowments and that as state supported institutions they had new responsibilities, Ross stated:

[17] C. M. Woodward, "New Opportunities for Secondary Schools," *Society for the Promotion of Engineering Education*, Vol. XI, 1903, p. 25.
[18] Earl D. Ross, *op. cit.*, p. 47.
[19] Edward D. Eddy, *op. cit.*, p. 118.

But acceptance of lengthened and expanded budgets came only with the growing recognition of the colleges as public service institutions that in curriculum and method, on and off the campuses, provided a new education for the new nation.[20]

Wellington's Controversy

Beginning March 19, 1892, and extending to June, 1893, A. M. Wellington published a series of articles on engineering schools of the United States in the *Engineering News*. Over and above the many statistics presented, the author used the articles to attack: (1) the Lawrence Scientific School for not living up to the conditions of its founder; (2) the extended summer vacations allowed to engineering students; and (3) the inadequate curriculum and over supply of mining schools to satisfy the needs of the mineral industry. Aside from letters-to-the-editor, the first two items attracted but little attention. Wellington's atack on mining education was particularly strong as the following quotations make clear:

> The average mining course as shown on the diagram would seem to be a most ill-judged course, from which no possible student can gain any advantage, unless he proposes to become a kind of scientific prospector.[21]
>
> As for mining engineering, what is there about the ordinary work of the ordinary mining engineer which requires a different training than that of a mechanical engineer? . . . the chief work of the mining engineer is to open and operate the mine advantageously; and the knowledge and experience of a civil or mechanical engineer gives just the right preparation for this kind of work. Such is the result in practice, evidently, for mining engineering itself is a rapidly expanding department of professional work, while the number of graduates from mining schools has been steadily declining since it reached its climax (of 61 graduates only) in 1884.[22]

The above and similar statements elicited rebuttal from Professor Monroe[23] in the form of letters-to-the-editor and from Professor S. B. Christy in an especially prepared article on mining schools. Monroe pointed out many errors in the figures from which Wellington drew his conclusions, and defined the difference in training functions to be performed. Christy showed that the increase in the number of mining engineering graduates just paralleled the increase in the total value of the mineral product of the country for the period discussed by Wellington. Christy suggested that mining education would probably best serve its needs by half a dozen outstanding institutions concentrating on the higher professional fields with the other schools gearing their programs

[20] Earl D. Ross, *op. cit.*, p. 180.
[21] A. M. Wellington, *op. cit.*, (Oct. 6, 1892) p. 328.
[22] *Ibid.*, (Aug. 11, 1892) p. 139.
[23] H. S. Monroe, "Letter Regarding Courses in Mining Engineering," *Engineering News* (Nov. 3, 1892) p. 415.

to the teaching of mining foremen.[24] An extended discussion of this controversy is given by Read,[25] who showed that although Wellington presented some figures of merit his analysis was incomplete and his predictions concerning the future of mining education were incorrect in view of the enrollments of the next two decades.

Society for the Promotion of Engineering Education

Organization.—A Congress of Engineering was held during the World's Exposition at Chicago in 1893. The success of the section devoted to engineering education was so great that a permanent organization named the Society for the Promotion of Engineering Education was founded.[16] The initial membership of seventy was composed of those that attended the Chicago meeting. It has been stated that the series of articles by Wellington were of great effect in causing the organizing of the conference on engineering education out of which grew the new society. In the next ten years, as the membership increased to 326, committees were formed to study such items as entrance requirements, statistics of engineering education, degree standardization and policies of common interest to all the schools.

It is of interest to note that the orginial membership of 70 increased to 156 in 1894. The latter figure, however, actually represented an average of approximately one and a half members for each engineering school. It was also small compared to the 1,747 A.S.C.E., 2,396 A.I.M.E., 1,662 A.S.M.E. and 768 A.I.E.E. memberships of the same year.[27] When the S.P.E.E. increased to 326 members in 1904 the aggregate of the above engineering societies increased to 11,960 as compared to 6,569 in 1894. The numbers are mentioned to indicate that the profession as a whole left the problems of engineering education to a relatively few school men. However, the work done by this zealous group was outstanding, as is indicated by the carefully prepared papers and reports contained in their annual publication. It was their work and the work of Wellington that justify the calling of this period from 1893 to 1907 the period of analysis in engineering education.

Classification of Schools.—In 1896 the report of a special committee on entrance requirements for engineering colleges set up a classification based on entrance requirements.[28] Although the classification adopted was not to be

---

[24] S. B. Christy, "The Growth of American Mining Schools and Their Relation to the Mining Industry," *Society for the Promotion of Engineering Education,* Vol. I, 1893, pp. 122-131.

[25] Thomas T. Read, *op. cit.,* pp. 128-134.

[26] C. Frank Allen, "Address of the President," *Society for the Promotion of Engineering Education,* Vol. VII, 1904, p. 12.

[27] Thomas T. Reed, *op. cit.,* p. 128.

[28] Report of the Committee on Engineering Degrees, *Society for the Promotion of Engineering Education,* Vol. XVIII, 1910, pp. 149-150.

taken as showing the relative general merits or standing, the colleges of the period were actually designated by these norms. The classification adopted and the number of schools in each class are given below:

> *Class A.*—Those colleges whose requirements for admission include at least Algebra through Quadratics, Plane Geometry, Solid Geometry, Plane Trigonometry, one year of Foreign Language, and moderately high requirements in English (31 Colleges).
> *Class B.*—Those colleges of the remaining list whose requirements include Algebra through Quadratics and Plane Geometry (31 Colleges).
> *Class C.*—Those colleges whose requirements in mathematics are lower than Algebra through Quadratics and Plane Geometry.
> *Class D.*—Those colleges that offer no courses in engineering as such, but do work analogous to that of an engineering college, generally under the head of mechanic arts.
> *Class E.*—Those colleges that have no entrance requirements as such, though doing engineering work of good grade. The system of education followed is so different from that of other institutions that they do not fit into comparison.

Degree Recommendations.—To give one further illustration of the work of the new society, the recommendation of its committee on degrees will be given. The degree problem was of long standing and the committee appointed in 1908 proposed the following recommendations to simplify the degree-granting practice:

> I. A four year engineering course should normally lead to the degree of Bachelor of Science (B.S.) to which should be added a specifying phrase, as for example: Bachelor of Science in Civil Engineering.
> II. The completion of an undergraduate course in engineering by a bachelor of arts should normally lead to the Bachelor of Science in Engineering and not to a Master's degree.
> III. The completion of a second undergraduate course in engineering by a bachelor of science should normally lead to the same degree, Bachelor of Science in Engineering with specification of the second branch and not the Master's degree.
> IV. One year of resident work in graduate engineering and scientific subjects by a B.S. in Engineering should normally lead to the Master of Science (M.S.) with the specifying phrase.
> V. The degree of Doctor of Philosophy, Doctor of Science, and Doctor of Engineering should be given for not less than three years of resident work in graduate engineering.
> VI. The professional engineering degrees of C.E., M.E., etc, should be given only to graduates who present satisfactory evidence of professional work of superior quality extending over not less than three years and submit a satisfactory thesis.
> VII. The same degree C.E., M.E., etc., may be given to engineers as honorary degrees; but great care should be exercised in awarding them.
> VIII. The degree of Doctor of Engineering, historically an honorary

degree may properly continue to be so regarded, though it is believed that as the work of engineering schools is extended and the granting of the degree in course becomes more frequent, its use as an honorary degree should dimish.

IX. Professional and honorary degrees should in general be different from those which are given in course.[30]

Industrial Training Courses

During the period covered in this chapter the large industrial concerns inaugurated training programs of their own. These programs were primarily for engineering graduates and stresses training in the art of engineering. The trainees were apprenticed to an organization as compared to the young civil engineer a century earlier who apprenticed himself to an individual. These courses were also open to a select group of non-engineering graduates who had certain practical experiences. In this way an avenue was open for the practical man to receive training and obtain status in the areas of design and management.

To illustrate one such course the following copy of the original outline of the General Electric Test Program that was started in the 1890's is given. For this copy the writer is indebted to Mr. J. B. Holmes of the General Electric Company.

GENERAL ELECTRIC CO.,
EXPERT DEPARTMENT

Prospectus of Students' Course in Practical Engineering

———————

The General Electric Company, having organized a Students' Course at their works at Lynn, Mass., and Schenectady, N.Y., for the purpose of giving young men a thorough, practical knowledge of electrical apparatus, presents the following information in regard to the same.

Two classes are provided for. To the 1st class are eligible young men of the age of 21 and upward who have graduated as a civil, mechanical, or electrical engineer from some technical school or college, or who have had two years experience in practical electrical work or two years machine shop work. An entrance fee of one hundred ($100) is required from each student of the 1st Class, and is to be paid to the Manager of the Expert Department within one week from the date of entry, and is only refunded should the student leave within thirty days of the date of entry. The rate of pay is 5c, 7c, 10c, 12c per hour for each period of three months.

[30] *Ibid.,* pp. 149-150.

The courses of instruction given at the different works are as follows:

LYNN WORKS

Kind of Work	Weeks
Shop Plant	
1. Wiring	4
2. Shop Motors	4
Arc Department	
1. Arc lamp assembling	2
2. Arc lamp setting	4
3. Arc machine assembling and testing	5
Incandescent Department, Direct	
1. Incandescent machine assembling and testing	4
2. Meters	2
3. Winding armatures	4
Stationary Motors and Generators	
1. Assembling and testing	4
2. Railway and large generators	5
Alternating Systems	
1. Machine assembling and testing	5
2. Construction transformers	1
3. Testing transformers	1
4. Testing mining drills and apparatus	2
Railway motor testing	3
Blacksmith shop	2
	—
	52

SCHENECTADY WORKS

Kind of Work	Weeks
Erection Department	
Assembling railway motors	2
Assembling small dynamos	1
Assembling large dynamos	1
Winding field magnets	3
Pillow block fitting, etc.	1
Tube Department	
Galvanometer work, testing Instruments, etc.	2
Wire Department	
Conductivity measurements	2
Testing multipolar armatures	2
Armature Department	
Winding and connecting armatures, Gramme ring	3
Winding and connecting armatures, drum	3
Testing armatures	2
Meter Department	
Railway Motors	3
Small stationary motors and generators	3
Edison Testing Department	
Testing large motors & Gen.	4
Use of instruments and general testing	4
F. & A. Department	
General machine work	2
Testing small motors, meter magnets, calibrating ammeters, etc.	4
Commutator work	2
Shop wiring & power station	4
Cable Department	
Testing insulation, etc.	4
	—
	52

Only one of these courses can be taken. In addition to the above the student may be required to do more or less work of an experimental nature, and the company reserves the right to vary the above as many times as may in its judgment be deemed best for the interest of both parties. Upon the completion of one of these courses in a satisfactory manner the student is given a handsomely engraved certificate testifying to his having passed through the course creditably. A nominal fee of two dollars is charged for this certificate.

Only a limited number of students will be received, and applications are acted upon in the order of their receipt.

The company does not guarantee to retain in its employ any student after the completion of the course above mentioned, and it also reserves the right to discharge any student for serious violations of its rules and regulations.

To the 2nd class are eligible young men who have graduated from a high school or its equivalent, who are at least 18 and under 20 years of age; the entrance fee being twenty-five (25) dollars subject to the rules mentioned above for the 1st Class. The course of instruction given to students of the 2nd Class is purely mechanical and preparatory to their transfer to the 1st Class, which takes place when they are 21 years of age, providing their work has been satisfactory. Assuming the student of the 2nd Class to be just 18 years of age on entering, his pay for the first year would be at the rate of 5c per hour, the second year 6c per hour, the third year 7c per hour, and on transfer to the 1st Class at the rate of 8c per hour for the first six months, then following the regular rate of pay of students of the 1st Class. No additional fee is exacted from students of the 2nd Class upon transfer to the 1st Class.

All students are required to observe the same rules, regulations and Hours of work as are set forth for the regular workmen of the factory to which they may be assigned.

In all cases satisfactory business references must accompany the application.

Applications should be addressed to James B. Cahoon, Manager Expert Department, General Electric Co., Lynn, Mass.

Continuation of Previous Trends and Policies

General Considerations.—The increased numbers studying engineering resulted from larger school enrollments, rather than from the establishment of new institutions. The 1896 Committee on Entrance Requirements of the S.P.E.E. recognized 110 schools. These numbers differed little from the 88 to 110 reported for the period up to 1893. With the number of institutions almost static, many schools attained larger enrollments in 1903, such as M.I.T. (1608), Wisconsin (582), Cornell (1196) and Rensselaer (950).[31]

With the exception of the University of Cincinnati, the institutional types remained unchanged. The basic four year course, operating under university standards with no centralized body of the profession formulating or enforcing educational policy, remained. Saville has termed this freedom from any dogmatism or obligation toward narrow professional objectives as the reason why

[31] Thorndike Saville, "Achievements in Engineering Education," *American Society of Civil Engineers*, Vol. C.T., 1953, p. 155.

engineering education has been adaptable to serve the nation's changing needs.[32]

The basic curricula, with their many degrees, adjusted themselves to meet the new conditions. So called "splinter" courses developed within the major branches, such as refrigeration engineering within mechanical, railroad engineering within civil engineering, and hydro-electric engineering within electrical engineering. The mining engineering course retained its single stem as it grew in popularity. As the courses increased, the percentage of specialized professional subject matter taught also increased.

Enrollment Characteristics.—Engineering enrollment statistics published in the yearly reports of the Commissioner of Education are limited to those voluntarily supplied by the institution. These figures, although incomplete, are all that are available and do indicate the enrollment trends. In these reports the enrollment figures for the various engineering branches are not given prior to 1899. Table 18 gives the engineering enrollment figures for universities, colleges, and technological schools as taken from the Commissioner's reports for the years indicated.

TABLE 18

ENGINEERING ENROLLMENTS IN THE UNITED STATES 1899-1906

Year	C.E.	Min.E	M.E.	E.E.	Ch.E.	Textl.	Gen.E	Total
1899	2,550	1,032	4,376	2,320	....	....	....	10,276
1900	3,140	1,261	4,459	2,555	....	....	....	11,515
1901	3,532	1,509	5,623	2,696	536	234	....	14,130
1902	4,754	1,837	6,363	3,203	858	68	....	17,083
1903	5,278	2,244	6,800	3,652	725	133	....	18,823
1905	7,356	2,547	6,654	5,204	759	138	1,893	24,951
1906	7,962	2,826	7,426	5,696	1,234	....	2,501	27,645

Table 18 indicates that civil engineering gradually regained its popularity without becoming the predominant engineering branch. The gradual increase of the mechanical, electrical and chemical branches are evident as is a renewed interest in mining engineering. With the exception of textile engineering, which was offered by Georgia Institute of Technology, North Carolina Agricultural and Mechanic Arts College, and Clemson Agricultural College the distribution of branches indicates a training for a national economy rather than for regional opportunities. A similar table made for the land-grant colleges would indicate a similar distribution, with the exception that mechanical engineering is fifty percent stronger than civil engineering. A land-grant college table would also show that approximately fifty percent of the total engineering enrollment is in the land-grant colleges.

As no figures are available, it is impossible to give the student mortality

32 C. Frank Allen, *op. cit.,* p. 12.

and the percentage of the freshman class that eventually received their degrees. It is known, however, that the percentage that graduated was small. In the year 1905, when the engineering enrollment was 24,951, only 1,204 received degrees, according to the Commissioner's report. Allowing for the fact that when this class entered in 1902 the enrollment was 17,085, the mortality still remains exceptionally high.

Technical Societies.—The increased number of engineering students was accompanied by an awakened professional consciousness. This was evident in the rapid growth in both the number of technical societies and in the membership of the previously existing ones.

Prominent among the new societies formed were the Society for Heating and Ventilation Engineers (1894), American Institute of Chemical Engineers (1904), the American Society of Refrigeration Engineers (1904), American Concrete Institute (1905), American Society of Automative Engineers (19-05) and the Illuminating Engineering Society (1906). The majority of these societies were known as splinter organizations. For instance, the Heating and Ventilation and the Refrigeration Engineers were offshoots or "splinters" of the American Society of Mechanical Engineers. This practice was strong and indicated that the founder societies were not catering to the changing professional interests of their membership. As a result, minority groups formed new societies that worked against the possibilty of developing a unity within the profession. However, it should not be inferred from this that the membership of the founder societies decreased. Actually they increased much faster than the population change for the period, as the figures in Table 19 indicate. The memberships given were taken from the transactions of the various societies for the years recorded.

TABLE 19
MEMBERSHIP IN THE FOUNDER SOCIETIES FROM 1894 to 1907

Year	A.S.C.E.	A.I.M.E.	A.S.M.E.	A.I.E.E.	Total
1894	1,747	2,396	1,662	768	6,569
1895	1,837	2,438	1,743	926	6,944
1896	1,927	2,412	1,748	1,023	7,110
1897	2,107	2,498	1,799	1,069	7,383
1898	2,107	2,417	1,876	1,102	7,502
1899	2,197	2,574	1,929	1,123	7,823
1900	2,227	2,661	2,064	1,183	8,135
1901	2,291	2,799	2,254	1,260	8,604
1902	2,603	3,267	2,425	1,549	9,844
1903	2,767	3,025	2,573	2,230	10,595
1904	2,931	3,262	2,740	3,027	11,960
1905	3,195	3,507	2,195	3,460	13,077
1906	3,359	3,680	3,040	3,870	13,949
1907	3,523	3,884	3,366	4,366	15,294

It is of interest to see that the increase in the number of members of the founder societies is approximately equal to the number of engineers graduated each year. To illustrate, the Commissioner's reports for the years 1907 and 1905 show 1,320 and 1,165 respectively, while in the same years the professional societies increased 1,345 and 1,117. It is not maintained that the graduates all became members but the fact is of interest.

Curricula of the Period.—The fourteen years considered was not one of curricula development. The trends established in the previous period continued with the major professional subject absorbing additional time.

The time distribution for the five major engineering curricula is given in Table 20.

TABLE 20

TIME PERCENTAGE DISTRIBUTION OF SUBJECTS FOR 10 ENGINEERING SCHOOLS IN 1907*

Curric-ula	Engineering		Draw	Shop	Mech & Hyd.	Sci. & Math.		Human-ities	Elect	Mil. Sci. P.E.
	Maj.	Other Eng.				Phy Sci	Math			
C.E.	32.9	4.4	6.2	1.7	9.8	14.4	12.3	14.4	1.7	2.2
Min.E.	23.0	14.4	2.4	.9	8.0	22.1	11.8	14.7	.9	1.8
M.E.	24.0	7.8	6.8	8.0	9.9	11.4	12.9	14.3	1.8	3.1
E.E.	24.0	12.2	6.5	5.4	8.4	11.0	13.4	15.1	1.2	3.0
Ch.E.	23.4	12.5	5.6	3.4	4.5	18.1	11.1	16.1	2.4	2.9
All Eng.	25.4	10.2	5.5	3.9	8.1	15.4	12.3	14.9	1.6	2.6
All Eng.	35.6					27.7				

*Evolutionary Trends in Engineering Curricula, *op. cit.,* p. 527-532.

The above table as compared to Table 12 shows that both the major engineering subject and the non-major engineering subjects were absorbing more of the time. This happened at the expense of the drawing, shop and humanity courses. From an engineering point of view, the civil engineering was almost complete in itself since students took practically no engineering courses outside of their department.

The trend toward teaching more of the practice of engineering at the sacrifice of the engineering sciences and the humanities was not supported by the studies of the time. Wellington's study of 3,500 engineering graduates in 1892 found that 59 percent were in strictly engineering work, others were in management positions involving engineering and 25 percent were in other occupations.[33] Fletcher in 1899 studied 6,000 engineers and substantiated the results obtained by Wellington.[34] In his study of a great variety of views,

[33] A. M. Wellington, " Supply and Demand of Engineers," *Engineering News* (Oct. 6, 1892) p. 329.
[34] Robert Fletcher, "The Present States of Engineering Education in the U. S.," *Society for the Promotion of Engineering Education,* Vol. VIII, 1900, p. 185.

Fletcher also found that there was a general consensus of 70 percent on the following points: do more work in fundamental subjects; teach thoroughly controlling principles which every engineer must fall back upon; develop practical sense and train the judgement, and attend only to such details as are essential; avoid side issues.[35] In 1908 Stienmetz commented:

> "It stands to reason that with the limited time at his disposal, it is inadvisable for a student to waste time on anything which he forgets in a year or two."[36]

In 1900 Raymond stated that there was too much differentiation among courses that required the same fundamental principles.[37]

In spite of the discusison of the advisability of asking for a broad and fundamental curriculum, the trend toward specialization continued in this period.

Changes in Established Patterns

The developments of the period were largely evolutionary, with expanding enrollments satisfying the new industrial needs. The new features that effected engineering education were limited to four. These changes were: (1) state support of engineering experiment stations at land-grant colleges; (2) the first state license law for engineers; (3) the introduction of cooperative education, and (4) the appointment of a committee, from engineering societies, to study the complete problem of engineering education.

Engineering Experiment Stations.—As late as February 27, 1896, Eugene Hale introduced into the first session of the 54th Congress a bill termed the "Hale Engineering Experiment Station Bill." It sought to establish engineering experiment stations at land-grant colleges to assist state industries as agricultural experiment stations had done. The bill was defeated, with the result that the individual states gradually established engineering experiment stations of their own. The first of these stations was established at the University of Illinois by action of the board of trustees in December, 1903.[38]

The second engineering experiment station was established at Iowa State College in 1904, with an appropriation of $3,000 to be expended solely for engineering experimentation and the publication of bulletins.[39]

The above land-grant colleges were the only ones to create engineering

[35] *Ibid.*, p. 186.

[36] Charles P. Stienmetz, "Electrical Engineering Elements," *American Institute of Electrical Engineers*, Vol. 27, 1908, p. 81.

[37] William Raymond, "The Promotion of Engineering Education," *Society for the Promotion of Engineering Education*, Vol. VIII, 1900, p. 191.

[38] L. P. Breckenridge, "The Engineering Experiment Station of the University of Illinois," *Society for the Promotion of Engineering Education*, Vol. XV, 1907, p. 558.

[39] G. W. Russell, "Engineering Experimentation at Iowa State College," *Society for the Promotion of Engineering Education*, Vol. VIII, 1900, p. 235.

experiment stations during the period and up to 1907. They are important since they signified the states' unwillingness to wait for federal support. The service they initiated was eventually copied by all land-grant institutions having engineering programs. The original philosophy of these stations has remained unchanged and is well expressed in the 1907 Iowa State College catalogue:

> "While the principle business of the several departments of the college is to give instruction to their students, the fact is recognized that the state contributes largely to the financial support of the college and that in return, not only should the college give tuition to the youth of Iowa, but it should contribute as much as possible to the successful carrying on of the industrial interest of the state."[40]

It should not be inferred that the only way a state school could assist state industries was through an engineering experiment station. Many of the colleges performed work previously started by other agencies of the state. Outstanding in this regard was the work on paving brick at Ohio and the hydraulic experiments at Cornell.[41]

Engineering State License Law.—The first registration law was enacted in Wyoming in 1907 as a result of the chaotic conditions which developed when homesteaders "surveyed" their water rights and signed their own names as "engineer."[42] Prior to this date two unsuccessful attempts were made to pass a similar law in Mississippi.[43] In 1908 Louisiana passed an act regulating the practice of Civil Engineering. At the time of its enactment it was stated that the public safety was being endangered by the practice of unqualified and sometimes unscrupulous persons, and that the law was essential and badly needed.[44] The two states of Wyoming and Louisiana were the only ones with engineering registration laws up to 1915. The license act of Wyoming made no mention of a college engineering course and gave several examinations of a profesional nature to qualify applicants for any one of five classifications. All classifications were concerned with phases of land surveying and hydraulic and irrigation engineering.[45]

The subject of license laws has been brought up to show that membership in one of the founder engineering societies did not carry with it a license to practice engineering as it did in Europe. The license laws also recognized

[40] *Ibid.*, p. 550.
[41] Ansen Marston, "Original Investigations by Engineering Schools, A Duty," *Society for the Promotion of Engineering Education*, Vol. VIII, 1900, p. 235.
[42] Ralph J. Smith, *Engineering As a Career*, (New York: McGraw-Hill, 1956) p. 38.
[43] Walter H. Drane, "Should the Engineer Be Required to Hold A License?" *Society for the Promotion of Engineering Education*, Vol. XVI, 1908, p. 350.
[44] Donald Dereckson, "History of Engineering Registration," *National Council of State Board of Engineering Examiners*, No. 81 (Dec., 1959) p. 5.
[45] Session Laws of the State of Wyoming, Ninth State Legislature, 1907, House Bill No. 63, Section 28, p. 147.

the value of professional experience in the art of engineering. Thus an engineering degree, or equivalent educational qualifications, had to be supplemented by accepted professional experience and an examination in both the theory and practice of engineering before a license was granted.

Cooperative Course in Engineering.—Between the years 1900 and 1906 Herman Schneider of the University of Cincinnati carried on an investigation to answer the following questions:

(1) What requirements should the finished product of an engineering school fulfill?

(2) Where and how shall we get the new material to make the required finished product?

(3) Through what processes shall we put the raw material in order to obtain a finished product?[46]

His investigation consisted of consultations with employees, graduate engineers, and students. He also visited large manufacturing concerns and studied their operations to determine the training needed for the young engineer going into industry. As a result of his analysis, he developed the cooperative plan of education as supplying the best solution to the problem of engineering education. This cooperative plan is defined as:

An integration of classroom work and practical industrial experience in an organized program under which students alternate periods of attendance at college with period of employment in industry, business or government. The employment constitutes a regular continuing and essential element in the educational process, and some minimum amount of employment and minumum standard of performance are included in the requirements for a degree. The plan requires that the student's employment be related to some phase of the branch or field of study in which he is engaged, and that it be diversified in order to afford a spread of experience. It requires, further, that his industrial work shall increase in difficulty and responsibility as he progresses through his college curriculum, and in general shall parallel as closely as possible his progress through the academic phases of his education.[47]

The experiment was tried at the University of Cincinnati with a six year program utilizing the same entrance requirements and the same basic instructional material as a regular four year course.[48] Each class was divided into two sections that alternated with each other, so that when one was in class the other was employed at their cooperative work, for which they were paid. This new type of engineering education was accepted rapidly during

[46] Herman Schneider, "Cooperative Course in Engineering at the University of Cincinnati," *Society for the Promotion of Engineering Education*, Vol. XV, 1907, p. 391.

[47] A Survey of Cooperative Engineering Education," Bulletin No. 15, *Federal Security Office of Education*, 1949, p. 1.

[48] Herman Schneider, "Two Years of the Cooperative Method," *Society for the Promotion of Engineering Education*, Vol. XVI, 1908, p. 29.

the next fifteen years and was one of the most original contributions made in the United States to the field of higher education. The complete program was original to this country although a method of sandwiching instruction and practice has been used in Scotland for more than fifty years.[49]

Proposed Comprehensive Study of Engineering Education.—Apparently the unorganized evaluation of the status and practices of engineering education initiated by Wellington, and those carried on by independent members and committees of the Society for the Promotion of Engineering Education stimulated a request for a comprehensive analysis of the subject. The S.P.E.E., which had 503 members in 1907, took the initiative through its president Dugald Jackson, by the following resolution:

> Whereas, it is desirable to make a comprehensive study of the objects and the utilities and the correct ideals of engineering education; therefor be it
> Resolved, that the S.P.E.E. hereby invites the respective governing boards of the A.S.C.E., the A.I.M.E., the A.S.M.E., and the A.I.E.E. and the A.C.E. each to appoint two members to become delegates composing part of a Joint Committee on Engineering Education; and further
> Resolved, that the Council of the S.P.E.E. is hereby directed to appoint three members as delegates to the membership of the said Joint Committee on Engineering Education and further
> Resolved, that the Joint Committe on Engineering Education shall be delegated to examine all branches of engineering education, including engineering research, graduate professional courses, and undergraduate engineering instruction, and the proper relations of engineering schools to the secondary industrial schools or foreman's schools, and to formulate a report or reports upon the appropriate scope of engineering schools, and that the said joint committee be requested to make a report of progress to this society within a year, and to make its final report to this society within two years (Report adopted).[50]

The preliminary report requested at the end of one year consisted of the following:

> Committee has not yet held a formal meeting. As the statistics needed are for the most part yet to be gathered it was suggested that the interests of the Carnegie Foundation for the Advancement of Teaching and the General Education Board be enlisted.[51]

The committe was given authority to enlist the services of the Carnegie Foundation and the General Education Board. Saville gives the reasons as to why the committee never completed the assignment defined for it by the resolution of 1907.

[49] William E. Wickenden, "Bulletin No. 16 of the Investigation of Engineering Education 1923-1929," *Society for the Promotion of Engineering Education,* 1929, p. 822.
[50] Resolution by the President, *Society for the Promotion of Engineering Education,* Vol. XV, 1907, p. 17.
[51] Preliminary Report of the Joint Committee on Engineering Education, *Society for the Promotion of Engineering Education,* Vol. XVI, 1908, p. 58.

The committee was organized, and the ASCE (in 1908) made an appropriation for its operation, the first recorded grant from an engineering society for an investigation of engineering education. However, the committee still lacked adequate funds for its investigation. In 1916, the chairman of the committee, Desmond FitzGerald, Past President and Treasurer of the ASCE, reported that "after we (ASCE) had spent all your spare cash in carrying on the work of this committee, we naturally turned our eyes to the Carnegie Foundation." The Carnegie Foundation undertook the task, and in 1918 issued a report by C. R. Mann entitled "A Study of Engineering Education."[52]

Concluding Statement.—This study on the "First Hundred Years of Engineering Education in the United States" terminates with the year 1907. This year was selected because for a number of years afterwards no significant changes took place in engineering education. This position is supported by the following statement that looked forward from the year 1909.

> There appears to be reasons why there will be a less strenuous growth in number and in material equipment; that in some respects, the technical schools of the country have reached a condition of comparative stability and during the next decade are likely to develop along other lines.[53]

The reason why they did not develop for some time along the other lines referred to is suggested by Scott in discussing the need for a comprehensive study on engineering in 1923.

> It was also realized that there has been a relatively static condition in engineering education for a decade . . . This relatively stabilized condition occurred while other groups of schools, some in fields related to engineering, were going through a period of rapid expansion . . .
>
> Engineering schools were undergoing no essential modification possibly because of the sound status already attained, although scientific research was productive and the growth of industry was unparalleled.[54]

---

[52] Saville, Thorndike, *op. cit.,* p. 156.
[53] Frederick E. Turneauve, *op. cit.,* p. 19.
[54] Charles F. Scott, "Report of Chairman of Investigation Committee," *Society for the Promotion of Engineering Education,* 1928, p. 1.

chapter 8

Conclusion

The first century of engineering education developed as a component of the complex American culture that evolved during this period. The various forces contributing to the final adoption of a four year college type of engineering curricula were many. To illustrate specifically the effect of these individual and social forces in engineering education, the question in the introduction of this book will be considered.

The Origins of the American Engineering School. — West Point and Rensselaer as the first two American engineering schools had the European characteristic of being founded separate from established colleges and universities. West Point, like the European military schools, was government supported, but unlike them it was founded to train civilian as well as military engineers. Rensselaer, founded in 1824 to train teachers of agriculture, gradually changed its objective as new needs developed. In 1828 it first mentioned engineering in its catalogue; in 1835 it offered a one year degree program in civil engineering; and in 1848 it extended its course to three years with a curriculum having French influences. Thus the origin of American engineering schools may be found in the practices of European technical schools that were adapted to meet American conditions and needs.

The Effect of the Traditional Colleges on the Development and Final Status of American Engineering Schools.—Prior to the civil war the classical colleges were not hostile to the teaching of science but were adverse to offering an engineering curriculum. The science and mathematics teachers helped train the majority of the faculty that later staffed the newly-founded engineering schools. Following the civil war, the classical college developed into the beginning of the modern American university with engineering as a division of its program. During this same time the provisions of the Morrill Act made the engineering school an integral part of the land-grant college. The endowed institutes of technology also assumed the basic college entrance requirements and the four-year structure of the college. Thus while the traditional colleges were in the beginning hostile to engineering education, they in the end set the pattern for the entrance requirements and the four year

163

under-graduate course. The evolution of the engineering curriculum indicates that up to 1870 the course differed little from a science course at the classical college.

The Establishment and Existance of American Engineering Schools As A Function of Initial Leadership and Local Support.—The establishment and continued existence of American engineering schools was dependent upon the following four distinct types of leadership during the nineteenth century:

1. Wealthy men of vision, who realized the need for engineers in the expanding American economy. These men, including Rensselaer, Gardiner, Lawrence, Sheffield, Cornell and Washburn, endowed many of our institutions without knowing much about engineering education.

2. Those pioneer educators who formulated and directed the instructional programs that determined the form and method of engineering education. This group included such men as Eaton and Green of Rensselaer, Eustis of Harvard, Thompson of Worcester, Thurston of Stevens, and Cornell, Wood of Michigan, Egleston of Columbia, Norton of Yale, Rogers of M.I.T. and Schneider of Cincinnati.

3. The group who sought by pamphlets, petitions, and legislative action to gain state support for technical training. Included in this classification were Buel of New York, Brown of Ohio, Turner of Illinois and Morrill of Vermont. These people desired to help the national economy and to raise agriculture and mechanic arts to the rank of a learned profession.

4. The college presidents who broke with tradition and incorporated engineering education as a part of the American college and university. Outstanding in this group were Nott Union, White of Cornell, and Tappan of Michigan.

The establishment and operation of American engineering schools was not accomplished by local support in the sense of using local tax money, or a large number of small donations. One exception was M.I.T., which was started from local funds obtained from a variety of sources. In a large measure the failure of the Gardiner Lyceum and Polytechnic College of Pennsylvania was due to the lack of local support. Basically the schools were founded and maintained by a few wealthy donors or by a combination of federal land endowments and individual state appropriations.

Growth of American Engineering Schools as Related to the Engineering Needs of Society.—Prior to the civil war the engineering schools were not meeting society's needs. To meet society's demands the majority of students either studied engineering in Europe, or attended West Point. The remaining engineers were imported from Europe, trained in the few engineering schools of the period or trained by experience. The large number of apprentice trained engineers justified the statement that the Erie Canal and the Baltimore and

Ohio Railroad were the outstanding engineering schools of the time.

Following the civil war, the number of schools and engineering students increased rapidly. As society became more complex, the engineering schools supplemented the single civil engineering course with curricula in mining, mechanical, electrical and chemical engineering as the needs arose. Up to 1907, the subdivisions of curricula continued to create splinter curricula such as sanitary and railroad from civil, marine and refrigeration from mechanical and hydro-electric from electrical. Distinct from the type of courses offered, the cooperative plan was introduced as an educational method to coordinate theory with industrial practice in engineering education.

Despite the many controversies centered on the engineering curricula, the supply and demand of engineers and the degrees offered, the number of schools increased rapidly up to 1890. From 1890 to 1907 (as the established schools became larger) the enrollments continued to increase more than two times faster than that of the population. Up to 1907 the engineering schools were basically teaching institutions with their products potential engineers whose numbers were sufficient to meet the needs of the times.

The Types of American Engineering Schools That Developed. — The three types of schools represented in the seven schools founded before the civil war established basic organizational forms for the 100 schools operating in 1907. These types consisted of the independent technological institute, the school of engineering connected with a college or university and a department of engineering in a college of arts and science. From the curriculum point of view such an individualistic approach as the combined mechanic apprentice engineering plan of Worcester was eliminated by 1907. This resulted in a more or less uniform four-year curriculum in the four basic professional divisions being offered by practically all the schools. The few exceptions to this were the Stevens school of mechanical engineering, the Thayer Graduate School of Dartmouth and the cooperative program at the University of Cincinnati.

The Establishment and Control of Engineering Education Differed From That of the Professions of Law and Medicine.—Law and medicine were recognized in Europe as learned professions and as such justified a faculty in the classical university. In America the legal and medical professions each developed a single national society that set the educational requirements for acceptance into these professions. Engineering, however, developed as many individual professions with a professional society being organized for each branch after school administrations had established a curricula in these divisions. Thus there were civil engineering graduates before an A.S.C.E. was established, mining engineering graduates before the A.I.M.E., mechanical engineering graduates before the A.S.M.E. and electrical engineering graduates before the A.I.E.E. This resulted in the type of engineering professional training being defined by the school men without a voice or control from a single profession. This practice had a strong influence in retaining the engineering program as a part of the four-year American college program as contrasted to the purely professional schools developed and controlled by the legal and medical professions.

The Evolution of the American Engineering Curriculum Up to the Year 1907.—The first degree programs in engineering were offered by Norwich and Rensselaer between 1835 and 1837. Rensselaer granted the C.E. degree for a one year course and Norwich the M.C.E. degree for a three year program. By 1870 the standard course was three years for a first degree as typified by Rensselaer, Columbia, M.I.T., and Illinois. These schools operated with a one year preparatory course that was eventually made the first year of a four year course as engineering adjusted itself to the four-year college program.

The curriculum changed from eight percent of professional subject matter in 1870 to thirty-six percent in 1907. The corresponding change in liberal art content was from sixty-four percent to forty precent respectively. By 1907 a standard curriculum was established that differed little regardless of types or geographic location of institutions. A few exceptions to this were the mining schools that catered to specific state needs, Arizona with its strong irrigation curriculum and Georgia Institute of Techonology with its textile engineering program.

Relation Between the Professional Engineering Societies and the Growth of Engineering Education.—There existed a parallelism between the growth of engineering education and the professional engineering societies. From a comparison of the two it can be seen that it was engineering education that lead the way. In all cases, branch engineering curricula were established before a corresponding society of practicing engineers was organized. Aside from the engineering meetings held at the Philadelphia exhibition in 1876 and at the Chicago exhibition in 1893, the professional societies exerted practically no influence on the administrative structure, curricula, entrance requirements, supply and demand of engineers or methods of engineering education. The meeting at Chicago in 1893 occasioned the founding of the Society for the Promotion of Engineering Education, which was organized distinct from the founder societies and kept the control of engineering education in the hands of the engineering educators.

The parallelism between curricula and professionalism was in numbers as well as in types of societies. This is illustrated by the 232 percent increase in founder society membership between 1894 and 1907 as compared to a 203 percent increase in engineering enrollments for the same period.

The Effect of the Morrill Act of 1862 on Engineering Education.—The large number of land-grant colleges established between 1865 and 1890 made engineering education under the title of "mechanic arts" accessible to the agricultural and industrial classes. Thus was successfully climaxed the fifty-year effort of many individuals and groups who, through pamphlets, petitions, memorials, reports and legislative bills, sought state support for technical education. On the other hand, the Morrill Act did little to initiate the distinctive form and character assumed by engineering education. By placing the teaching of mechanic arts in the college it added another link to the chain that attached engineering programs to the four-year undergraduate program with its entrance requirements geared to the secondary school system.

Probably one of the major contributions of the act lies in the fact that it was a declaration of faith with respect to the practical application of democratic ideals to the cause of higher education. It gave tangible evidence of the willingness of both federal and state governments to support agriculture and mechanic arts without excluding other scientific and classical studies needed to promote the liberal and practical education of the industrial classes in the several pursuits and professions of life. In realizing this objective, engineering or "mechanic arts" developed in response to state initiative and never received national support as did agricultural education. There was no United States Department of Mechanic Arts created or no federal act passed to create and support engineering experiment stations. Without federal support, however, the states recognized the need for research in engineering and created engineering experiment stations at the land-grant colleges.

The Relation Between the Growth of American Public Education and American Engineering Education.—Prior to the civil war West Point and the few engineering schools in existence operated without much dependence on the Latin school, the academy or the public high school of the time. The higher institutions prepared their own students by a one year preparatory course that was operated in conjunction with the three year engineering school. The increased number of high schools eventually caused the discontinuance of the preparatory departments with the extra-year being added to the engineering course of study.

Since the public school was basically an urban institution, the land-grant colleges had difficulty obtaining qualified students from the agricultural areas. To cope with this problem preparatory departments were again operated by the colleges. These new preparatory departments were to meet mininum entrance requirements for a four-year course of study. These preparatory courses gradually disappeared following the rapid expansion in secondary school enrollments from 1890 to 1910. In this period secondary enrollments increased 400 percent faster than the population while engineering enrollments increased only 200 percent.

INDEX